BIRDS OF OUR GARDENS

BIRDS OF OUR GARDENS

ENID BLYTON

Cover illustration by Christopher A. Sinden
Text illustrations by David Pratt

A Piccolo Book

PAN BOOKS LTD : LONDON

First published 1940 by George Newnes Ltd.
This edition published 1973 by Pan Books Ltd.
33 Tothill Street, London, SW1.

ISBN 0 330 23536 2

Printed in Great Britain by
Richard Clay (The Chaucer Press), Ltd, Bungay, Suffolk

Contents

Preface

DEAR CHILDREN,

Most of you love birds, and would like to know them all, especially those that come to your garden every day. This book is written for you, so that you, like Mollie and Tony in the story, may easily get to know your friends, the birds in the garden. All the things spoken of – the bird-table, the peanut feeder, the tit-bell, the seed-hopper, the lucky-bag, the coconuts, the nesting-boxes, and the roosting-places, can be obtained by you quite easily. Most of them can be made, but in any case, not one of them is expensive, and you could put them down on your birthday or Christmas list, if you would like to do the same things that Mollie and Tony do in the story.

I do hope you will make a bird-table, and buy a coconut and some peanuts! You will have such fun with them, and the birds will soon be tame and become your friends.

Good luck from your friend,

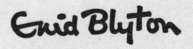

CHAPTER ONE

The Little House in the Country

'I WONDER what Uncle Jack's little house in the country will be like,' said Tony, looking out of the carriage window as the train sped along.

'It's quite old, Mummy said, and has a most exciting garden,' said Mollie. 'There's a pond, and at the bottom there is a little wood with bluebells in the springtime.'

'I wish Mummy and Daddy were coming with us,' said Tony. The two children had just said goodbye to their mother and father at Southampton, and had waved goodbye to them as the big liner on which they were sailing steamed slowly away. They had gone to America for a whole year, and Tony and Mollie were to stay with their aunt and uncle in the little village of Meadowfield.

'I guess it will be dull at Meadowfield after living in London,' said Mollie. 'It's a good thing Auntie Jane and Uncle Jack are so nice.'

'We shall soon be there,' said Tony. 'It's the next station.'

They were met by their Uncle Jack, a tall, jolly-faced

man in boots and breeches like a farmer. He was waiting with the pony-cart, which was a treat for the children. They scrambled in, and Uncle Jack lifted in their trunk.

'Well, here you are at last,' he said. 'Welcome to Meadowfield and to Sparrow Cottage!'

Sparrow Cottage was a little brown house with a nice thatched roof. 'What a funny name!' said Mollie, laughing.

'Well, don't you think it looks rather like a little brown sparrow, sitting there waiting for crumbs?' said Uncle Jack with a smile.

'I suppose we are the crumbs?' said Tony, and they all laughed.

'And you are Jack Sparrow!' said Mollie to her uncle. 'Yes — it's a good name, Uncle. I like the little brown house.'

'We only moved in a month ago,' said Uncle Jack. 'But it's quite ready for visitors. Look! There's your aunt waving to you.'

Aunt Jane had opened the door and was waving and calling to them. 'Welcome to Sparrow Cottage, children!'

The two children ran to their aunt and hugged her. Then in they all went, and Aunt Jane took them up to their snug rooms under the thatch. There were two tiny rooms there, one for each child.

'They do feel nice and old and friendly,' said Mollie, pleased. 'Shall I unpack now, Aunt Jane?'

'No, come down and have tea,' said her aunt. 'It's all ready for you — hot scones on a cold day like this.'

So down they went after they had taken off their outdoor clothes, and washed. There was a bright fire in an old brick fireplace, and the scones were sitting in the fender, keeping warm. The long, low window looked out on to the garden.

There was a green lawn first, with beds on each side, and in the middle of the lawn was a pond. At the bottom was the little wood, its trees almost bare of leaves, for it was November.

They all sat down to tea. The children sat so that they could see the garden. It seemed strange to be looking out on green grass and trees, instead of on to roads full of buses and cars.

'It does seem quiet here, after London,' said Mollie. 'I miss the roar of the buses.'

'Well, dear me, I was thinking it was very noisy here this afternoon,' said Uncle Jack. 'I can hear the fantail pigeons cooing next door, and there's a thrush up there singing because he thinks he might as well try his voice, and that robin on the bush has been carolling ever since we have been in the room.'

'Really?' said Tony, in surprise. 'Well, I haven't heard any of that! Have you, Mollie?'

'No,' said Mollie, listening hard. 'I can't hear any birds at all. We didn't in London, either.'

'Well, it would be difficult to hear a bird singing in a crowded London street,' said Uncle Jack. 'But here it is one of the commonest and loveliest sounds. Surely you can hear that robin now, Mollie?'

'I really can't,' said Mollie. 'And I'm not a bit deaf, either.'

'Jack, it's because the children are not used to listening for the birds,' said Aunt Jane, pouring out more tea for Tony. 'When they have been here a few days they will soon tune their ears up and hear all kinds of sounds they cannot hear now.'

'Well, I hope they will,' said Uncle Jack. 'They are missing a great deal, if they can't hear the birds. But I know that a lot of people don't hear them. Most extraordinary!'

'Look at that chaffinch!' said Aunt Jane, nodding her head towards the window. 'Isn't he a beauty?'

The children looked out. They saw a few brown birds on the lawn that looked all the same to them.

'What's a chaffinch?' asked Mollie. 'All those birds look like brown sparrows to me – only they are cleaner than our London ones.'

'My dear Mollie!' said Uncle Jack, quite shocked. 'In that little group of birds you are looking at, is one cock chaffinch, one hen chaffinch, two house-sparrows, one hedge-sparrow, and, nearer the pond, a song-thrush.'

'Good gracious!' said the two children in astonishment.

'What! So many different birds,' said Tony. 'But how do you know, Uncle? I wish they'd come nearer, then I could perhaps see that they are different.'

'There's a crow!' said Mollie, suddenly, wanting to show her uncle that she knew one bird, anyway. A big black bird had perched in a nearby tree.

Uncle Jack gave it a glance. 'It's a jackdaw,' he said. 'It's not big enough for a crow or a rook.'

'I thought crows and rooks were the same,' said Tony.

'Jane, these children don't know the first thing about birds,' said their uncle. 'What are we to do with them?'

'You must teach them, Jack,' said Aunt Jane at once. 'They are sharp children, and would love to learn to make friends with the birds. Wouldn't you, Mollie and Tony?'

'Oh, yes!' said Mollie. 'I once held a tiny yellow chick in my hand and I loved it – it was so warm and soft. I'd love to make friends with all the birds here.'

'So would I,' said Tony. 'It is silly to be surrounded by birds and not know one from another! Could you teach us about them, do you think, Uncle Jack? Daddy has often said what a marvel you were with birds. He has told us how you and he knew the eggs and nests of all the birds when you were boys, and how you used to pick up the tiny nestlings from their nests and feed them yourselves, and tame them.'

'Yes,' said Uncle Jack. 'We had wonderful times, your father and I. And we'll have wonderful times again, this year, you and Mollie and I. I shall have some fun showing you all I know.'

'You can begin tomorrow,' said Aunt Jane. 'It's too late today – it's getting dark already.'

'Right,' said Uncle Jack. 'We'll start making friends with the birds tomorrow morning, children. And we'll bring the birds close to us so that you can see them easily and well, and will soon known all our commonest birds.'

'But how will you bring them close, Uncle?' asked Mollie.

'You wait and see!' said Uncle Jack.

CHAPTER TWO

Making the Bird-Table

AFTER breakfast the next morning the two children followed Uncle Jack outside. There was a small gardening-shed beside the house, and in it were all their uncle's tools, pots, boxes, straw, and many other things. It was an exciting place.

'What are we going to do, Uncle?' asked Tony.

'We are going to make a bird-table,' said Uncle Jack. 'We will put it as close to the window as we can, and then, when the birds come to it, you will see them very closely. Now, let me see – we want a good stout pole – a long one. Can you see one anywhere about?'

'There's this old broken clothes-post,' said Tony, pulling out a long post that Aunt Jane had once used to hold up her clothes-line when it was full of clothes. 'Would this do?'

'Yes – fine!' said Uncle Jack. 'Just the thing. I think it's long enough to raise the table out of the reach of cats. Now we want a nice flat piece of wood that will do for the top of the table.'

He soon found one. It was a good strong piece of wood that had once been the lid of an old box. Uncle Jack and the children took the pole and the wood into the garden.

'Now to drive the pole into the ground, just here, near the window,' said Uncle Jack. He dug a hole in the ground and then drove the post down into it. Then he and the children packed the earth back, and stamped on it to make it firm.

'Now we'll nail the top piece on,' said Uncle Jack. 'Get the hammer and nails off the shelf in the shed, Tony.'

Tony nailed the top piece to the post, and then shook the table. It was firm and stong.

'Is that all, Uncle?' asked Mollie.

'Well, this is all that is necessary,' said Uncle, 'but I think we'll nail a little rim to three sides of the table, so

The simplest bird-table of all – a flat piece of wood
nailed to a post

that on a windy day the food won't easily blow off. We'll look in the shed for three narrow pieces of wood to make an edge.'

They had to use the saw to cut a long piece of batten wood into the right lengths. Then they nailed the three pieces to the edge of the table to make a nice rim.

'Why don't you put an edge to the fourth side, on the front of the table?' asked Mollie.

'Can't you guess?' asked Uncle.

Tony could! 'Because sometimes you'll want to clean the table,' he said, 'and it would be difficult to scrape off the bits if the table had a rim all round.'

'Quite right!' said Uncle Jack. 'We must clear the table of bird-dirt and old bits of food each day, and we can easily scrape them all off this unrimmed side with a piece of

Children's bird-table with a rim round three sides,
and twigs for the birds to perch on

wood. And now – one more thing and the table is finished.'

'What's that?' asked Mollie, puzzled.

'Birds often like to perch on twigs before hopping down to the table,' said Uncle Jack. 'They are used to twigs, and also they look pretty, sitting on little branches, waiting to hop down on to the table. We'll go and get some from my little wood.'

So down they went to the wood at the bottom of the garden. Uncle Jack broke some twiggy sprays from the hazel trees there, and took them back to the table. With small tacks he nailed the twigs to the back of the table.

'There!' he said. 'Our bird-table is quite ready. It didn't take us long to make, did it? It is nice and high, too so that no cat can jump up on it and catch the birds.'

'But you haven't a cat, Uncle,' said Tony.

'No, but other people have,' said Uncle. 'Plenty of cats wander into our garden, and we can't really blame them for catching the birds, because it is their nature to catch birds and mice – but we can prevent them from catching the birds on *our* table.'

'Uncle! There *is* one thing the bird-table still needs,' said Mollie suddenly.

'What?' asked Uncle Jack.

'Food on it,' said Mollie. 'Let's go and ask Aunt Jane for some.'

'We'll have to hurry up with the food,' said Tony. 'It's going to pour with rain. Come on, let's get it!'

CHAPTER THREE

The Visitors

THEY all went indoors and found Aunt Jane making a pudding for dinner.

'We want something for the bird-table, please, Aunt Jane,' said Mollie.

'Well, what birds do you want to see first?' asked Aunt Jane.

'Oh! Do birds eat different food then?' asked Mollie in surprise. 'I thought they all ate the same – worms and things, you know.'

'Indeed, they don't!' said Aunt Jane. 'Some birds never touch worms, and other birds never take any seed. Jack, what do you want to put on the table first?'

'Well, we haven't any hemp-seed or sunflower-seeds or nuts,' said Uncle Jack. 'It had better be any scraps you have, Jane. We can watch the birds that come for those, and then perhaps tomorrow I could take the children to buy seeds and nuts. We could go hunting in the woods and hedges for berries too. That would be fun!'

'Well, I've got a few crusts of bread over there,' said

Aunt Jane. 'And there are a few old dog biscuits in that bag that must have belonged to the dog who was here before we came. And there is a bit of cold potato in the larder. That's all you can have today – unless you like to have the milk pudding scrapings after lunch. The blackbirds love those.'

'We'll take all you've got,' said Uncle with a laugh. 'Mollie, here are the dog biscuits. Put them to soak for a little while – the birds like them that way. And this very dry bread had better be soaked too. These crusts are not so bad – they are off this morning's toast. They will do as they are. Here, Tony, take the potato – that will be a treat for some of the birds.'

It wasn't long before the bird-table was spread with a good feast – soaked dog biscuits, the stale potato, the soaked bread, and the crusts.

'Now come indoors and sit quietly by the window and watch,' said Uncle Jack. 'I insist on your learning at least four of our commonest birds today. First of all – where's my bird-book? If you see pictures of the birds at the same time as the birds themselves it is a great help in remembering them.'

Uncle got his bird-book. It had a good many coloured pictures in it. The children sat quietly on the window-seat and watched the bird-table, which was just outside. For a long time no visitor appeared at all.

'Be patient,' said Uncle, when they began to fidget. 'All wild birds and animals are scared of new things, and are cautious at first. I can hear some sparrows on the roof talking about the bird-table and wondering if they dare to go down to it.'

'*Can* you, Uncle?' cried Mollie. 'I can't hear a thing.'

'Well, Mollie, sit perfectly quiet and think of the roof

just above you,' said Uncle Jack. 'You will hear the sparrows chirruping there.'

Tony and Mollie sat quite still and listened. And both of them suddenly heard the excited chirrups of the half-dozen sparrows on the thatch above.

House-sparrows

'I *do* hear them now!' said Mollie delighted. 'But why ever couldn't I hear them before, Uncle?'

'You didn't exactly know what to listen for,' said Uncle Jack. 'You can train your ears to hear more and more sounds, you know, Mollie. It's just a matter of always keeping them open, and really *listening*. Ah – look! There's our first visitor.'

A small brown sparrow had flown down to the bird-table. He perched on a twig first and then hopped boldly down to the food. No sooner had he pecked a little up than down flew the rest.

'The sparrows are always the first,' said Uncle Jack. 'They are not very friendly birds, but they are bold and cheeky. See how well they keep a look-out in case a cat comes. Their bright eyes are everywhere.'

'Aren't they enjoying their meal?' said Mollie, pleased. 'What thick, strong beaks they have, Uncle Jack! And look at the little white specks at the top of their wings. What are they saying to one another? It sounds like "Philip! Philip!" to me.'

'A good many people have thought that,' said Uncle Jack, smiling. 'And the little brown bird is often called Philip Sparrow because of his call. Oh, Mollie! – why did you do that?'

Mollie had suddenly raised her hand and rubbed the window-pane. She had been breathing on it and made it misty – but her sudden movement had frightened the sparrows and sent them all flying away, chirruping noisily.

'Oh, I'm sorry!' said Mollie, in dismay. 'I didn't mean to frighten them.'

'Any sudden, sharp movement scares birds and animals,' said Uncle Jack. 'You will always find, Mollie, that the people who make friends with the wild creatures are those with gentle movements and a quiet voice – no rough-voiced person with sudden, sharp movements ever gets to know the wild creatures well.'

'Look – they are coming back again,' said Tony. 'Keep your hands down, Mollie, for goodness sake. Oh, Uncle, what's that big bird that has flown right down on to the table?'

'That's a song-thrush,' said Uncle Jack. 'Do you see his speckly, freckly chest, Tony? You will always know a thrush by the freckles he wears. There is another thrush too, much bigger, not so neat-looking as this one, called a mistle-thrush or storm-cock. He often sits at the top of a tree and sings wildly in a storm. That is why we give him the name of storm-cock. You can tell he is a thrush, like his cousin there on the table, because he, too, wears freckles on his chest.'

The song-thrush

'This song-thrush is very pleased with the potato,' said Mollie. 'Look at him pecking it up. He keeps looking at us with his big eyes, Uncle – is he afraid?'

'No – but he doesn't really trust us,' said Uncle. 'Ah, look – here comes a bird who really *does* trust us – the only one of our birds who really seems to prefer the company of man to the company of birds.'

The children saw a red-breasted robin fly down to the twigs at the back of the bird-table. He perched there for a minute or two, flicking his wings and looking sideways with his big black eyes at the window-pane.

'He doesn't really like feeding with the others,' said Uncle Jack. 'He prefers to have the bird-table to himself.

The robin looked at the children

Ah – something has frightened the birds again. I think this time you'll see the robin is back first. Once he has made up his mind that it is safe, he will be on and off the table all day long.'

Uncle was right. The robin did come back first and pecked at the soaked bread eagerly. As soon as the sparrows flew down again, he was off! He sat on a nearby bush and warbled out a delicious little song.

'His voice is very *creamy*, isn't it, Uncle?' said Mollie.

'A very good word for it, Mollie,' said her uncle. 'Your ears are getting sharp already.'

'Uncle! There's another bird – it's black – is it a jackdaw again?' asked Tony.

The blackbird with his glossy black feathers

'No – it's much smaller than a jackdaw,' said Uncle. 'It's an easy bird to remember – it's just a blackbird. See his yellow beak, and his glossy black feathers? He's a beauty. He is one of our most beautiful songsters, too – some people say the loveliest of all our feathered singers.'

'Will he sing now?' asked Mollie.

'No – not till the early spring days,' said Uncle. 'Then you'll hear him – and all the other birds too. I hope your ears will be well-trained by then, because I shall want you

to be able to tell me which birds are singing even if you
can't see them.'

'I'll never be clever enough for *that*!' said Mollie.
'Uncle, that's four birds we know already. The red-
breasted robin with his long thin legs, his bold black eyes,
and scarlet breast. The little brown sparrows with their
thick beaks and brown coats. The thrush, a big bird with a
freckled chest and brown back – and – and what's the other
one?'

'The blackbird, silly,' said Tony. 'He's still on the table,
look. Doesn't he gobble the potato?'

'Well, four birds are enough to learn in one day,' said
Uncle Jack. 'Tomorrow we will go and buy some other
kind of food and see if we can get more visitors still.'

CHAPTER FOUR

Going Shopping. More Visitors

THE next morning Uncle Jack took the children into the next town in the pony-cart to do their shopping. They went first to a seed-merchant and Uncle Jack asked for some hemp-seed for the birds.

'Won't you have mixed seed?' asked the shopman. 'They like that.'

'I know they do,' said Uncle. 'But mixed seed will grow in the cracks of my crazy-paving path and everywhere else it blows, too – but hemp-seed doesn't. So hemp-seed it must be, please, or my garden will be full of strange weeds. I'll take a good deal, because it is cheaper that way.'

'And is there anything else, sir?' asked the shopman, doing up a big bag of hemp-seed.

'Yes – have you any sunflower-seeds?' asked Uncle Jack.

'Plenty,' said the shopman. 'Old Mrs Brown's parrot has those, and I keep a good store.'

'I'll take the same amount of those then, please,' said Uncle Jack. 'A quarter of a hundredweight. That will last us a very long time – and will be much cheaper than buying a pennyworth at a time.'

'Now we'll go to the fruit shop,' said Uncle when they had put the two big bags into the cart.

'Are we going to buy fruit for the birds?' asked Mollie in astonishment. 'Do they eat bananas and apples, Uncle?'

Uncle laughed. 'We're going to buy *nuts*,' he said. 'Peanuts, which the tits love, though I expect you call them monkey-nuts. Brazil-nuts, also for the tits. And a nice big coconut.'

When they had all the things they wanted they drove back home again. 'Are we going to put all those things on the bird-table now?' asked Mollie.

'No,' said Uncle Jack. 'No nuts today – just the seed, I think. Oh, and some bacon rind and a bone, if Aunt Jane has any.'

Aunt Jane produced six strips of bacon rind and a large mutton bone with some fat on it. 'Thanks,' said Uncle Jack. 'I think we shall tempt some more visitors to our bird-table today.'

The children scattered some hemp-seed on the table, and a good many sunflower-seeds. Mollie put the bacon rind on, and Tony put the bone in the middle. More bread crusts and crumbs were scattered, and the scrapings of a milk pudding.

'Now let's come indoors and watch,' said Mollie. 'Look, Tony – the sparrows are already collecting on the roof and there's the robin over there.'

'And there's the blackbird,' said Tony. 'They are all waiting.'

Soon they were sitting on the window-seat to watch. The brown sparrows flew down. The robin flew up to the twigs. The blackbird came along, and the thrush sat on a nearby bush and watched to see what was going on. He had just eaten a very large worm and did not feel hungry.

'Ah – here's a new visitor,' said Uncle Jack.

'Where?' said Mollie, astonished.

Food that you may easily get for your bird table: nuts, bird seed, coconut, wheat

'On the table, Mollie,' said Uncle. 'Can't you see?'

'No,' said Mollie. 'Can you see a new visitor, Tony?'

'Well – I think I can,' said Tony. 'But it's awfully like the sparrows, Uncle. Do you mean that little neat brown bird at the end of the table there?'

'But that's a sparrow,' said Mollie.

'Well, it doesn't really belong to the sparrow family,' said Uncle, 'although its name might make you think it does. It is called the *hedge*-sparrow, because in colouring it is like a house-sparrow. But it isn't a bit like the cheeky house-sparrow, really. It is quiet and timid. And now just look at its beak. It is much more like a robin's, isn't it – thin and long – than like the blunt, thick beak of an ordinary sparrow.'

The hedge-sparrow

'Oh – now I'm beginning to see the difference, Uncle Jack!' cried Mollie. 'Look how it flicks its wings, Uncle – it is always moving them.'

'You are sharp-eyed, Mollie,' said Uncle Jack, very pleased. 'The bird has another name – shufflewing – because of its fidgety habit of flicking its wings. It has a third name too – the dunnock.'

'Does it chirrup like the sparrows?' asked Tony.

'No,' said his uncle. 'It says "peep, peep!" and has a pretty high-pitched little song which you will often hear if you listen. Now that it has found our bird-table it will come to it often and you will get to know the hedge-sparrow very well indeed. He is really a dear little bird.'

'Oh, look – there's a simply *lovely* bird!' cried Mollie, and she was so excited that she pointed. At once all the birds flew away, the sparrows chirrupping in alarm.

'Oh, Mollie, you *are* silly!' cried Tony angrily. 'Now they've all gone.'

'They'll come back again,' said Uncle Jack. 'Mollie will soon remember to move gently, Tony. Don't scold her. *You'll* forget in a minute, I expect – and off they'll go once more.'

'Oh, there's that lovely bird back again,' cried Mollie, seeing a pink-chested bird fly down to the table. 'It's a bit like a sparrow, Uncle, because its beak is thick and strong – but it has a different-coloured chest.'

'It's a chaffinch,' said Uncle. 'In the springtime its chest will become a very beautiful bright pink indeed. Do you see the bright white patch on its shoulder, Mollie?'

'Oh, yes,' said Mollie. 'And look, Uncle, there's another bird with him, with that white shoulder-patch – but its chest is light brown.'

'That is Mrs Chaffinch,' said Uncle Jack. 'She doesn't have the pink chest – but you can always tell her by her white shoulder-patch and very neat appearance – almost as if she had just washed and brushed herself ready for a meal.'

'The chaffinches are certainly much neater-looking than the sparrows,' said Tony. 'I can tell them easily. And now, look – there's another bird – quite a big one – and another – and another – all the same!'

'Starlings,' said Uncle. 'I was wondering when they would discover the bacon rind and the bone. They love fat of any sort. Watch them squabble!'

The starlings *did* squabble. They were really very funny indeed. They wore blue, green, and purple feathers, but these were not so bright and shiny as in the springtime. They looked rather spotty, and their tails were short and stumpy. They perched on the bone, pecked and pulled at

The cock chaffinch has a pretty pink chest, but the little hen is brown

it, called angrily at one another, and tried to buffet each other away with outspread wings.

They made Mollie and Tony laugh very much. The starlings' voices were shrill, and not very musical, and they certainly made a great noise.

'The starling is more of a talker than a singer,' said Uncle Jack, as they watched the excited birds. 'But he does try *so* hard to sing. He sits on a chimney-pot, opens his yellow beak, and tries to pour out a song like a blackbird.

Starlings have spangled coats and talk a great deal

But all that comes from him is wheezes, chuckles, bubbles, and clicks. You'd laugh to hear him.'

'The starlings have scared the other birds away with their noise and roughness,' said Mollie. 'They are like a gang of rough boys scaring quieter children from their toys.'

'You're right, Mollie,' said her uncle. 'There are some birds, such as the robin and the hedge-sparrow, who like to go by themselves or in pairs – and there are others, like the house-sparrows and the starlings, who love to be in flocks. Now, tell me – did you notice what food our new visitors ate today?'

'Yes,' said Mollie at once. 'The hedge-sparrow ate the soft food, the chaffinches ate the hemp-seed – and the starlings liked the bone and the fat.'

'Good, Mollie!' said her uncle. 'Did you notice that the

house-sparrows ate the seed today, too? Did you see how their strong beaks, and the chaffinches' strong beaks too, cracked those hard seeds? That is why they have those thick, cone-shaped beaks – because they are mainly seed-eaters.'

'We know seven common birds now,' said Tony. 'I can say them to you, Uncle. Listen. House-sparrow, robin, song-thrush, blackbird, chaffinch, hedge-sparrow – and starling!'

'We *are* getting on!' said Uncle Jack. 'Don't forget the difference between the hedge-sparrow and the house-sparrow, will you?'

'Oh, no – if I remember that the hedge-sparrow is the shufflewing, and shuffles its wings, I shall always know it,' said Tony. 'Besides, it has a thin beak like a robin, not a thick beak like the other sparrow.'

'How can you tell the chaffinch from the sparrow?' asked Uncle Jack, suddenly turning to Mollie. But the little girl was not to be caught.

'It has a pink chest and a white shoulder-patch, Uncle,' she said. 'Ha, ha! You can't catch *me*!'

'Now we'll look at all our new friends in my book,' said Uncle Jack. 'A picture will stay still to be looked at – and a bird won't. Tomorrow we will put out our nuts, and we will hope for some more new visitors. There are still plenty more to come. And we will put out a saucer of water too – all birds drink water, and a good many of them love to bathe in it. You can get an enamel saucer from your aunt, Mollie. Don't forget!'

CHAPTER FIVE

The Acrobats on the Coconut

NEXT day Mollie put an enamel dish of water on the bird-table, as well as all the scraps that Aunt Jane gave her. Before she spread the table, she cleaned it well, scraping it with a piece of wood. She scraped the dirt into a sheet of newspaper, and then put it into the dustbin.

Tony scattered the hemp-seed and the sunflower-seeds. The birds were waiting all over the garden for their breakfast, longing for the children to go, so that they might fly down to their feast.

'What about the coconut, Uncle?' asked Mollie, when she had finished.

'Yes – we'll hang that up now,' said Uncle Jack. 'There is a tree branch just by the window, and we'll hang it there. Then the birds will come right to the window.'

'What birds?' asked Tony.

'You'll soon see,' said Uncle. He went to the shed to get his hammer.

'Are you going to crack the nut in half?' asked Tony. 'Or will you hang it up whole?'

'Well – which shall we do?' asked Uncle. 'If I tap the nut all round – like this – and then give it a very hard blow with the hammer, the nut will fall in two halves fairly evenly. We can then hang up the two halves – *upside down*, not the right way up, though!'

'How funny! Why?' asked Tony.

'I think *I* know,' said Mollie. 'It's because the rain might collect in the halves unless you hang them upside down – and the nut would go rotten.'

'Quite right, Mollie,' said Uncle. 'Now, if we *don't* break the nut in half, but simply make little holes at each end, the birds will not only be able to use the nut for food – but, when it is empty, they will creep inside the coconut and use it for a roosting-place on cold nights.'

'Oh, would they really?' cried Mollie, pleased to think of tiny birds sleeping in an empty coconut shell. 'I could put a few bits of moss inside for them, to keep them warm.'

'You could,' said Uncle. 'Well – which is it to be – two halves – or one whole?'

'I think we'll have one whole nut this time,' said Mollie. 'I'll buy the birds another nut later on myself, and we'll cut that in halves.'

So Uncle Jack knocked a hole in each end of the nut. There was coconut milk inside, and Tony drank half of it, and Mollie drank the other half.

Then Uncle Jack took some strong string and tied the coconut up to the branch that grew near the side of the window.

'In half an hour, at the most, you will see that the news has spread, and the birds will come flocking back to our nut,' he said. 'Now – where are those other nuts? Come indoors for a moment, children, and do a bit of work for me.'

They went indoors. Uncle Jack gave each child a stout needle and a long string. 'I want you both to thread a long string of peanuts for me,' he said. 'Then you shall each hang one outside your bedroom window. I'll thread one too, and hang it from the front of the bird-table.'

So they all threaded the nuts busily. It was rather hard work to push the needle through the yellow shells of the peanuts, but before very long the three of them had got strings of peanuts ready. Then Uncle Jack cracked three or four brazil-nuts. He tied each one to a piece of string about a foot long.

'Why don't you put the nuts loose on the bird-table, like the seed?' asked Mollie.

'You'll soon see,' said Uncle Jack.

They looked out of the window – and, dear me, what a sight the bird-table was! 'I wish I could count how many birds there are there, but I can't, they keep moving about so!' cried Mollie. 'Sparrows – *two* thrushes, Uncle – the little hedge-sparrow again, flicking his wings as usual – ever so many starlings on the old bone again!'

'And the chaffinch has brought his wife once more,' said Tony. 'See the white patch on their shoulders? The robin isn't there. He is waiting till the table is empty, then he will eat proudly by himself.'

'Look, Uncle – what are those little blue and yellow birds perching on the twigs?' said Mollie, suddenly. 'They are new visitors. See – one is on the bone, pecking away hard.'

'Ah – that is one of the visitors that will come to our nuts,' said Uncle Jack. 'It's a tit. Look – here he comes to the coconut now. I told you it would soon be discovered!'

The tiny bird flew to the coconut. It pecked away at it, with its head inside one of the holes. Every now and again it jerked its head out and looked quickly around for enemies.

Then another tit flew to the nut, and went to the other side. Then a third flew up, and stood on the top, chattering away crossly, raising the feathers on its head up and down, up and down.

Great-tit and blue-tit on the coconut

'Are they all tits, Uncle?' asked Tony, watching them in delight. 'Oh, look – that one has swung upside down on the string!'

'Yes – they are all tits,' said Uncle, 'and the tits are the acrobats of the bird-world. They can eat upside down and swing about in any position.'

'But, Uncle – they look different to me – not all the same. Are you *sure* they are all tits?' asked Mollie. 'Look –

that one has a bold, black cap on his head – but that little, smaller one, has a *blue* cap.'

'Good girl, Mollie,' said Uncle Jack, very pleased. 'Yes – although there are three tits on our nut, they are all different. The blue-capped one, with his yellow, green, and blue dress is the little blue-tit or tom-tit. You will hear him calling "pim-im-im-im-im, pim-im-im-im-im!" in the springtime. Now look at the biggest tit of the three – do you see his lovely black head and bib? He is the great-tit, because he is so big. You will hear him calling "tea-cher, tea-cher, tea-cher!" in the springtime, and sometimes "pink, pink!" very like a chaffinch does.'

'What about the third little fellow?' asked Tony, watching him as he pecked hard at the nut. 'He is small and his coat is dull.'

'Yes,' said Uncle. 'That is the coal-tit. He isn't so pretty – and you will *always* know him by the white streak at the back of his neck. Do you see it?'

'Oh, yes,' said Mollie. 'Neither of the other tits have that white neck-stripe. I shall always know the coal-tit by that. Uncle, the three tits looked so alike at first – but now I can tell each from the other very easily.'

'Then you are already cleverer than most grown-ups,' said Uncle Jack. 'Hardly any grown-ups know the tits from one another. Look, Tony – here's another tit visitor – which one is it?'

Tony took a quick look. 'It's a blue-tit,' he said. 'Look at its pretty blue cap. You can't catch *me*, Uncle! Are there many more tits who will come to our nut?'

'No more that will visit the nut,' said Uncle Jack. 'But some very pretty little tits visit my small wood each autumn, flying in flocks. They are called long-tailed tits, because they have such surprisingly long tails. Look – here

Coal-tits enjoying a few peanuts

is another coal-tit. How do I know him, Mollie?'

'Easy,' said Mollie at once. 'You can see his white streak at the back of his head. What does he say when he calls in springtime, Uncle?'

'He says "if-he, if-he, if-he!" ' said Uncle. 'You will hear them all calling and singing later on. Get to know them well now, and you'll soon learn their calls.'

'What about these peanuts and brazil-nuts?' asked Tony. 'Can we go and hang them up?'

'Yes,' said Uncle. 'We'll have a bit more fun then.'

Uncle Jack hung a string of pea-nuts from the front of the bird-table, and then hung the brazil-nuts there too, each dangling on its own bit of string. Then they all went indoors again to watch.

A bold great-tit was the first to see the brazil-nuts. He

Two long-tailed tits and their nest

said 'pink, pink!' very loudly and flew to the edge of the table. He looked over it, down to the nut swinging below, his head on one side. Then, to the children's great delight and astonishment, that tit hauled up the nut 'hand over hand' like a sailor, till it pulled it on to the table. It pecked it with joy.

'How clever!' said Mollie. 'Oh, look – there's a blue-tit, Uncle. It isn't pulling up the nut, it's swinging on it, upside down. Look – the nut's swinging round and round and the tit is swinging round too. It will get giddy!'

'Oh, no, it won't,' said Uncle Jack, laughing. 'It is an acrobat, as I told you. Acrobats never get giddy. Now, see – the coal-tit has found the peanuts. Watch it hammer away at the shell to get at the nut inside.'

Soon there were three tits on the string of peanuts, which swung and twisted with the weight of the little birds. They soon tore away the yellow shells and pecked at the sweet nut inside. The great-tit dropped the brazil-nut, and neatly hauled it up again. Three other tits pecked away at the big coconut; and really, the children hardly knew which to watch!

'It's as good as going to the cinema,' said Mollie. 'Uncle, why doesn't *everybody* hang up nuts in wintertime?'

'I really can't imagine,' said Uncle.

CHAPTER SIX

A Neat Little Fellow

ALL that day the children glued their noses to the window-pane to watch the dozens of birds that ate and quarrelled and drank. 'I do love to see a bird drink,' said Mollie. 'Look at the robin drinking, Tony. He puts in his little black beak, and then lifts his head up high – and lets the water trickle down his beak into his throat. He opens and shuts his beak quickly all the time as if he is tasting the water.'

'And look – now he is bathing in our dish!' said Tony excitedly. 'Uncle, come and see. The robin's having a bath.'

But before Uncle could come, another small bird flew down to the bird-table, perching on the twigs first. The children cried out in excitement, for it was a new bird.

'Uncle – quick! There's a new visitor. He is making the robin leave the dish. He's standing in the water himself on long legs. Who is he?'

Uncle looked. 'A water-wagtail,' he said. 'One of the neatest and prettiest of all our birds. He is dressed in black and white, as if he were a little gentleman, going out to an evening party! He loves to paddle in water – which is why we call him water-wagtail.'

'I know why he's called *wag*tail,' said Tony. 'His tail is never still.'

'But he isn't really *wagging* it,' said Mollie, watching him closely. 'He's *nodding* it, Uncle, up and down, up and down; not from side to side like a dog.'

'You're quite right, Mollie,' said Uncle, 'he should really be called nodtail, not wagtail. Isn't he a neat little fellow! You should see him in the springtime, darting after flies, running for all he is worth, and then doing a little jump into the air after them.'

'Yes – he runs – he doesn't hop like the sparrows,' said Mollie, watching the wagtail run across the table. 'That's funny. Why doesn't he hop?'

'You will find that those birds who live mostly in the *trees*, such as the sparrows, nearly always hop,' said Uncle Jack. 'You see, they have to put their feet close together to hop from twig to twig – so they keep up the habit on the ground and go on hop-hop-hopping there. But birds that spend most of their time on the ground, such as the water-wagtail and the fantail pigeons next door, prefer to walk or run. Some birds do both. Watch the blackbird. You'll see him give fine long hops sometimes – and then he will suddenly run.'

'I shall always look and see whether a bird hops or walks or runs now,' said Mollie.

'The wagtail is our very smallest running bird,' said Uncle. 'Look at him pecking away at the bread. He won't touch the seed. His beak is not strong enough to deal with hard seeds.'

'He's having a bath now,' said Tony. 'Uncle, birds are

sweet when they are drinking or having a bath. Look how he puts his head under the water and tries to shake the drops over himself with his wings and head.'

The wagtail was enjoying himself. The November sun shone down on the bird-table, and the neat little bird felt

Pied wagtail

hot. The water was cool and fresh. He scattered silvery drops all over himself and the table too. Some fell on to the chaffinch who primly shook them off.

'We shall have to fill the dish again,' said Mollie. 'How pleased the birds must be to find food, drink, and a bath all in the same place, Uncle.'

The wagtail flew out of the bath. The robin at once hopped in and he, too, bathed himself well. The wagtail shook the water from his feathers, and cried 'chissic, chissic!' very loudly.

'He said "chissic, chissic!" ' said Mollie, laughing. 'Is Chiswick where he lives?'

The others laughed. 'Well, if he lives at Chiswick, as he says, he's come a long way to get here,' said Uncle. 'Let's hope he won't go back, but will stay with us to amuse us with his nod-nodding tail and his morning bath.'

CHAPTER SEVEN

Three Lovely Visitors

THE children thought that the chaffinch was one of the prettiest of their visitors, and they asked their uncle, if the rest of the finch family were as pretty.

'Oh, some are prettier,' said Uncle at once. 'I've been hoping we might get the loveliest of the lot – the beautiful bullfinch with his deep red breast and black velvet cap. Then there is the dainty goldfinch, a fairy-like bird, who may perhaps come if we string up some seeding michaelmas daisies or thistle-heads. And the clumsier greenfinch, with the gold patches on his wings. He loves the wild seeds of the fields and hedges.'

'Well, can't we go out and collect some?' asked Mollie. 'It would be fun! We could pick berries, too, Uncle, couldn't we? The birds love those, you said.'

'Very well. It's a lovely morning. We'll go out seed-hunting,' said Uncle. 'Bring a tin with you, each of you, and I'll take a basket for berries.'

So off they all went. It really was fun. The children bent down low to see if any of the half-dead plants had seeds they might take. A good many of them had. They soon had quite a collection in their tins. Uncle was busy too. He picked some thistle-heads full of down and seeds. He picked sprays of hawthorn-berries and stems full of the scarlet rose-hips. He picked up beech-mast from the floor of the woods.

Food you can get from the woods and hedges for the birds: thistle-heads, beech-mast, hips, yew-berries, elder-berries, and haw-berries

'The birds will have a fine collection to choose from,' said Mollie, shaking the seeds in her tin.

'When there are a great many berries, Aunt Jane picks them and dries them,' said Uncle Jack. 'Then she uses them in a cake for the birds.'

'A bird-cake!' said Mollie in surprise. 'Oh, how lovely! Do you think she would bake one for our bird-table?'

'I should think so, if you ask her,' said Uncle. 'Last year Aunt Jane picked and dried elder-berries, yew-berries, privet-berries, and mountain-ash berries. My word, you should have seen how the birds enjoyed them when they were put into one of your aunt's bird-cakes!'

'I never knew there were so many exciting things to do,' said Mollie. 'I shall ask Aunt Jane to teach me to make bird-cakes tomorrow.'

When the children's tins were half-full of wild seeds, and Uncle really couldn't get any more thistle-heads and berries into his basket, they went back home.

It was fun to tie the thistle-heads and the berry-sprays on to the twigs at the back of the bird-table. It was jolly to tip the wild seeds into a shallow saucer and set them by the twigs.

'Now we'll see if we get any of the other finches,' said Uncle. 'Come along indoors.'

That day they only got one new visitor – the goldfinch! He brought with him three other goldfinches, the prettiest, most fairy-like birds that the children had ever seen.

The goldfinch saw the ripe thistle-heads, and flew down to the twigs. He loved the thistle-heads. He called to his companions, 'twit-wit-wit-wit-wit-wit!' It was a pretty liquid call. They all came darting down from the trees, with a pretty, jerky flight. They hung on to the thistle-stems and pecked busily at the heads.

'You can easily tell the goldfinch from any other finch,' said Uncle Jack. 'Do you see his striking red, white, and black head, and that brilliant gold band on his wing?'

'Yes – and I can tell he is a finch because he has the same thick, coneshaped beak of the chaffinch and the sparrow,' said Mollie. 'Aren't they enjoying the thistle-heads!'

The pretty goldfinches pecked the down from the heads

The goldfinch

busily. Then, at a sudden noise from the lane outside, they all rose together and flew to the tree, twittering.

'A flock of goldfinches is called a "charm",' said Uncle Jack. 'It's a good name for them, isn't it – for they really are charming.'

The next morning, whilst the children sat at breakfast, Uncle Jack nodded towards the window. 'Do you see what I see?' he asked. 'Mr Bullfinch and his wife!'

The children stared in delight. Yes – there was the cock bullfinch sitting on the twigs behind the table – and on the table itself was his wife, pecking up the wild seeds that the children had collected.

'Isn't he lovely!' said Uncle. He certainly was. He had a beautiful brick-red breast, very rich in colour, and a lovely blue-black velvety head.

'He's all red and black,' said Tony. 'Oh, Uncle, did you

see that? He flew down to the table and kissed his wife!'

'Yes, he did,' said Uncle Jack. 'Bullfinches are very affectionate birds. They keep to the same mate all their life, and go about together the whole year round. Now, look – they are going to have a bath!'

Two bullfinches. They are loving birds, and keep their mate for life

As the children were watching the two birds, Uncle Jack pricked up his ears and listened.

'I can hear greenfinches now,' he said. 'They are in the old ash tree, sitting in a flock. Look – down they come!'

As the greenfinches flew down to the bird-table, the bullfinches flew off. They did not like being with other birds. The greenfinches set to work to eat the seeds and the yew-berries.

'I should know they were greenfinches even if you

hadn't told me, Uncle,' said Mollie. 'They have the usual thick finch beak – and they are green. But what a pretty yellow band they have on their wings! Not so golden as the goldfinch, but very bright.'

The cock and hen greenfinch

'And there's a little bit of yellow under their tail too,' said Tony, who was getting as sharp-eyed as Mollie.

'Your visitors have better table-manners than you have, Mollie and Tony,' said Aunt Jane, with a laugh. 'You've let your bacon and eggs get quite cold – really, anyone would think you don't like the nice breakfast I've cooked for you!'

'Oh, Aunt Jane, we *do*,' said Mollie, beginning to eat again. 'But Uncle Jack's bird-table is more interesting than his *breakfast*-table just at present. Aunt Jane – will you make us a cake tomorrow?'

'Why, I made you one yesterday!' said Aunt Jane in surprise.

'Yes, but this time we'd like a different sort of cake – one for the birds,' said Tony. 'A bird-cake, Aunt Jane.'

'Oh – so Uncle Jack has been telling you about my maize-cake, that I make for the birds each winter, has he?' said Aunt Jane, laughing. 'Very well, I'll make one for you tomorrow – and you shall help me.'

'Oh, good,' said Mollie. 'We shall have to make a big one, Aunt Jane, because we have such a lot of guests to feed now. Sparrows, robins, thrushes, blackbirds, hedge-sparrows, starlings, chaffinches . . .'

'Great-tits, blue-tits, coal-tits,' chanted Tony.

'And wagtails, goldfinches, bullfinches, and green-finches!' cried everyone together.

'We *do* know a lot!' said Tony.

CHAPTER EIGHT

Making the Bird-Cake

'Now, Auntie,' said Mollie next morning. 'What about that bird-cake? Tony and I have cleaned the bird-table and spread it with food, and put fresh water into the dish. The birds are having a fine time – but they say they *would* like a cake!'

'Dear me, you seem to understand their language very well, all of a sudden,' said Aunt Jane, laughing. 'Come along, then, both of you – you shall make the maize-cake.'

Aunt Jane put a big bowl on the kitchen table. She went to the store cupboard and took out some paper bags and tins, Mollie peeped into them.

'What's in these tins and bags?' she asked.

'This is maize meal,' said Aunt Jane, shaking a large amount of it into the bowl. 'It is very cheap. You can buy it at any seed-merchant's. The birds love it.'

She took another bag and opened it. 'You know what *this* is,' she said, as she shook out the little brown seeds.

'Hemp-seed!' said Tony. 'It is what we put on the bird-table each morning.'

'Yes,' said Aunt Jane. 'And these little, round hard seeds in the tin are millet-seeds. Seed-eating birds really *love* those. Open the next tin for me, Tony, will you, and we'll put a little of the canary-seed mixture inside into the bowl too.'

Preparations for the bird-cake

'Can we help to mix all the seeds together?' asked Mollie, looking into the bowl. Aunt Jane nodded. Then the two children put in their hands and scrambled them about till the seeds were all well mixed. They liked feeling the little hard seeds running through their fingers.

'Now I want you to chop up some nuts for me,' said Aunt Jane. 'There are peanuts in that big bag – and there are brazil-nuts on the dish in the dining-room. Go and fetch seven or eight, Tony.'

Soon the children were very busy chopping up the nuts

with Aunt Jane's little kitchen knives. It was fun, though they had to be very careful not to cut their fingers.

'Now put the chopped-up nuts into the bowl,' said Aunt Jane. 'You have chopped them up nice and small.'

Into the bowl went the nuts too. 'What next?' asked Mollie. 'It looks a good mixture, Aunt Jane.'

'I've got some fat melting in that pan on the stove,' said Aunt Jane. 'Last week's dripping. We pour that over the whole mixture next.'

'Let *me*!' cried Tony. But Aunt Jane shook her head.

'No,' she said, 'children are not allowed to play about with boiling fat. *I* shall pour it in. If I hadn't any fat, I would use boiling water.'

'Aunt Jane, let's put in a few currants too,' said Tony suddenly, seeing a bag of currants on the dresser. 'I should think the berry-eating birds would like those.'

'They would,' said Aunt Jane. 'The thrushes and blackbirds never say "No" to a currant. Very well, empty some in whilst I get the fat.'

Tony shook in a good supply of currants, and then he and Mollie gave the mixture a last stir. Up came Aunt Jane with the pan of boiling fat. She poured it in carefully over the mixture, stirring with a long spoon.

'There!' she said. 'Our cake is made.'

'Do we cook it now?' said Mollie.

'It doesn't need to be cooked,' said Aunt Jane. That's the nice part about this cake. I just put the whole mixture into a cloth and let it dry. Then, when it's dry, I shall take off the cloth, and cut a slice from the cake whenever you want one for your birds.'

'Will it keep, then?' asked Mollie.

'All the winter,' said Aunt Jane. She took an old teacloth and emptied the mixture into it. Then she tied it all up tightly, and gave it to Tony to go and hang up in the garden-shed till it was dry.

'Then you and Mollie shall take off the cloth and see your bird-cake,' she said.

'Oh, Aunt Jane, isn't it easy to do!' cried Mollie. 'I'm surprised that more people don't make cakes for the birds. It's fun!'

'They would if they knew about it,' said Tony. 'I shall tell everybody now. Come and put it in the shed, Mollie. Thank you very much, Aunt Jane!'

When the cloth felt perfectly dry, in a day or two's time, the children unwrapped the cake.

'Oh, isn't it lovely!' cried Mollie. 'It's hard and knobbly – and look, you can see the seeds and the currants all over it!'

'It's a funny shape,' said Tony. 'But that doesn't matter. Let's take it to Auntie and show her.'

They carried it carefully to Aunt Jane. She gave them an old enamel plate to stand it on. 'Now you shall cut the birds a slice for their table,' she said. 'Mollie, you can cut the first slice, and Tony can cut a slice tomorrow.'

Mollie cut a good slice. It really looked delicious. 'I wish I could have a bite,' she said.

'No, you mustn't,' said Aunt Jane at once. 'It is not meant for children. It is always dangerous for girls and boys to eat food prepared for animals or birds. For one thing, there might be berries in a bird-cake – I often put them in if I have some by me – and yew-berries, for instance, are very poisonous to children.'

'Let's put the slice on the bird-table,' said Tony. So they laid it in the middle. Then they went to the dining-room window to watch.

All the birds loved the bird-cake! The sparrows and

finches pecked the seeds out of it. The tits pecked at the chopped-up nuts. The blackbirds and thrushes took the currants, and the starlings like the fat. Even the robin came to have a taste. It was fun to watch them all.

No new bird came that day – but so many of the others came, especially sparrows and starlings, that the children really couldn't count them.

'I think our bird-table must be the most crowded one in the country,' said Mollie, And it certainly was!

CHAPTER NINE

Roosting-Places

THE weather became very cold. Frost came each night, and in the morning the ground was white.

Aunt Jane kept a big fire in the house, and when the children went out they were warmly wrapped up.

'We shall have to put fresh water on the table ever so many times a day,' said Mollie to her uncle. 'I put some out this morning when I fed the birds, Uncle, and in about twenty minutes time it was frozen again.'

'It is important to give the birds water in this sort of weather,' said Uncle Jack. 'You see, all the puddles are frozen, our garden pond is covered with ice, and I expect the lake not far off is frozen too. More birds die of thirst than of hunger in this weather. So many people are kind in giving them food – but not everyone remembers to put out water as often as they can.'

'Well, Uncle, what shall I do?' asked Mollie. 'The water freezes *so* quickly.'

'Do you see how the frost has melted over there, under that hedge?' said Uncle suddenly, pointing to a bare patch of earth by a thick hedge. 'It's a sheltered spot there, facing south – what about putting a dish there, full of water? It will freeze at night – but it will be all right in the daytime.'

'Good idea,' said Mollie, and she went carefully to the hedge, carrying the dish of water. Certainly the frost had melted just there – so it must be a warmer spot than up on the bird-table. Mollie scattered some crumbs nearby so that the birds would see the water and go to it.

They were very grateful They soon discovered it and came to take drinks. The thrush even had a quick bath, and then flew up to the ash tree to dry himself.

Then the children began to worry about something else. Their Aunt had told them that she had put an extra blanket on their beds to keep them warm at night – and that made them think of the birds.

'Nobody gives *them* an extra blanket,' said Tony. 'Uncle, where do birds sleep at night?'

'Usually in the thickest hedges and trees,' said Uncle Jack. 'The evergreen trees are very useful to the birds in the winter – because they are not bare like the other trees. But, even so, on a cold night with bitter frost, some poor little birds are frozen to the bough they roost on. The tits are sensible – they roost in holes if they can. I told you that they would roost in empty coconut shells, didn't I? They will roost in flowerpots too.'

'Uncle, have you any empty coconut shells?' asked Tony.

'Yes – I believe there are some old ones in the shed,' said Uncle. 'We'll get those, shall we, and hang them here and there in the rose-ramblers. We'll get some flower-pots too, and you and Mollie shall find good hidey-holes for them in the hedges.'

Soon the empty coconut shells were hidden in the

ramblers, here and there. Tony and Mollie found some moss and dried it by the fire. Then they stuffed it into the shells.

'It will be a kind of blanket,' said Mollie.

Birds cuddling together under the porch

Then they took some small flower-pots and tucked them into odd corners of the garden – in a hedge, in the fork of a tree, in a bush. They put each pot on its side and stuffed a little hay inside.

'Turn the open side of the pot away from the cold north and east,' said Uncle Jack. 'No bird will creep in there if a bitter wind blows at him all the time!'

The children felt pleased to think that they had given the birds such warm beds, when night-time came, for the frost was bitterer than ever. Aunt Jane kept the fire piled high for it was the coldest night of the year.

'Would you children like to see something rather lovely?' asked Uncle Jack suddenly, putting down the book he was reading.

'Oh, yes – what is it?' asked the children.

'Well, I've just heard a little scrabbling noise up in the thatch,' said Uncle Jack. 'And that means some of our birds have crept under the eaves and are roosting there. I'll get my torch and show them to you.'

The children put on their coats, hats, and scarves. Uncle Jack took a torch and led the children to the garden door. Over this door was a porch, thatched like the rest of the house. Uncle Jack raised his torch and shone it above the children's heads.

The porch roof was lined with wood, and in the wood were little holes. 'That is where the birds get in,' said Uncle Jack. 'They squeeze in under the thatched eaves too. Now watch whilst I gently move this loose board, and we'll look into the hollow place under the thatch of the porch. Stand on the wooden seat there and you'll get a good view.'

The children stood on the old wooden bench in the porch. Uncle Jack deftly slipped out the loose board and shone his torch into the hole. 'Don't make a noise,' he said to the children.

They said nothing at all – but their eyes grew round with delight. Cuddled together under the straw thatch of the porch were about twenty little birds. Mollie counted six tits. There were a great many sparrows too. They blinked at the light with their black eyes, but did not move.

'Isn't that a lovely sight?' said Uncle Jack, switching off his torch and putting back the loose board. 'Now I'll show you where the wrens roost. You haven't seen the wren on the bird-table, but I expect you will one day.'

Uncle Jack took the children outside the dining-room

window and switched his torch on again, so that they could see the thick end of the thatch. In it were small holes, some going back a long way into the straw.

'The cock wrens make these holes,' said Uncle Jack. 'They begin a great many nesting-places before they at last choose one for their nest – and in the wintertime they use the holes for roosting in. Look – can you see that little brown wren cuddled at the back of the hole there?'

Holding their breath, the children peeped into the hole. At the back was a tiny wren, startled by the light. It made no movement at all.

In the next hole there was a little wren too. They were sweet to see.

'Uncle, *could* we see if there are any birds in our coco-nuts and flower-pots?' asked Mollie. 'Do let's!'

'Well, see that you don't get cold then,' said Uncle. 'It's a bitter night.'

The three of them looked into the coconut shells. In the first one a blue-tit looked out at them. He had surrounded himself with the dry moss and looked as cosy as could be.

'Oh, Uncle!' whispered Mollie in joy. 'Isn't he warm and snug? Oh, I *am* glad we thought of this!'

The next coconut shell was empty – but in the third were *two* tits – coal-tits this time, for Uncle Jack could see the white streak at the back of their heads. They were cuddled up side by side. One little bird opened its eyes in the sudden light of the torch, but the other was too fast asleep even to peep at them!

'Now for the flower-pots,' said Uncle. 'Where did you put them?'

The children remembered. What do you think was in the very first one, down on the ground under the hedge? The robin! He had made himself very comfortable in-

deed in the hay and had his head tucked under his wing.
His red breast shone in the light.

'We won't disturb him,' said Uncle and he switched off
his torch. In the next pot was a wren, and in the next, two
sparrows had squeezed. They flew out as soon as the light
shone. 'Never mind,' said Uncle. 'They'll go back again
when we've gone.'

Robin building his nest in a flower-pot

Only one pot was empty. 'That's because you put it facing the north,' said Uncle, pushing it round so that it faced
the other way. 'The icy wind blows from the north tonight,
and no bird will roost with that blowing in on him. Well –
what do you think of the birds' sleeping-places? Rather a
fine sight, don't you think so?'

'Yes – it was lovely,' said Mollie, thinking of the robin
with his head under his wing, and the other tiny birds

looking in surprise at the unexpected light of the torch. 'Listen, Uncle! I'm sure I heard something stirring in this big yew bush.'

Uncle Jack cautiously parted the green sprays and pressed his torch inside. Cuddled close against the trunk was a song-thrush, with his speckled breast showing up clearly in the light. He took his head from under his wing as the light caught him. Higher up was another thrush, looking scared. He hopped to the other side of the bush.

'Well – we won't disturb them,' said Uncle Jack. 'All over the countryside tonight birds are huddled in the warmest places they can find – behind the ivy on the wall, in holes and nooks, in the thickest evergreens. And now I think we'd be sensible if we go and do the same – find our nice warm beds and cuddle down into them.'

So indoors they went, and after a hot cup of cocoa and milk they all went up to bed. And when they cuddled down under their warm blankets and hugged their hot-water bottles, the children thought gladly of the roosting-places *they* had given the birds. It was lovely to think that a few birds were warm and safe that night because of the children's own kindness.

CHAPTER TEN

The Birds' Christmas Tree

THE month of December was bitterly cold – but just as Christmas week came along, the north wind dropped and a breeze blew from the south-west.

'That's good,' said Tony, who was beginning to know the winds very well. 'We shall get rain – and it will be warmer for Christmas – though it would be fun to have some snow!'

'Oh, I expect we'll get some snow if these clouds stay very long,' said Uncle Jack. 'They bring rain now that the wind has changed – but if it gets any colder they will send snow instead.'

'I've been trying to think what I can give the birds for Christmas,' said Mollie, 'but I can't think of anything except a new enamel dish for their water – and they really won't notice that!'

'We'll give them a Christmas tree of their own,' said Aunt Jane. 'I've ordered one for you two children and I'll order a small one for the birds too. Uncle Jack and I will dress *your* tree – and you shall dress the birds' tree.'

The children stared in the greatest surprise. Then they laughed.

'You don't really mean it, do you?' said Mollie. 'I've never heard of a tree for the birds before. Whatever should we put on it – trains and dolls and drums?'

Everybody laughed. 'No,' said Aunt Jane. 'Not things like that, Mollie, as you very well know – but other things that they will love and that will be a treat for them. Uncle Jack will tell you what to buy, if you have any money for the birds.'

The children had some money between them which they had saved for the birds' Christmas present. Uncle Jack took them shopping and they bought quite a lot of things for the tree.

First they bought long sprays of millet-seeds at the seed-merchants. They had already bought millet-seeds loose by the pound for Aunt Jane to make another bird-cake, but now they bought the sprays in which the millet-seeds grew – long, seed-filled sprays, out of which the ripe millet-seeds dropped every now and again.

They bought another coconut. They bought a half-pound packet of Osborne biscuits – the sort with little holes in them. They bought some more brazil-nuts, but no peanuts because they still had plenty in their store at Sparrow Cottage.

'Good gracious, Uncle! Are we going to put all these things on the tree!' cried Mollie. 'How queer it will look!'

The little Christmas tree had arrived by the time the children were ready to dress it.

'Cut up the coconut into pieces about three or four inches big,' said Uncle. So they did that – and then Uncle pierced each piece with a small knife, and the children threaded strong thread or string through the hole, tied it round the piece of nut in a knot, and then hung each piece of coconut from a twig of their small tree. Soon there were about fifteen pieces of coconut hanging from the tree!

'Now we'll tie the millet-sprays on the tree too,' said Mollie. So she and Tony tied up the three millet-sprays they had bought. They hung down from the tree, their little round seeds tumbling out now and again. They were simply full of seed – Mollie thought there must be thousands of seeds in each spray!

Then they threaded strings of peanuts and looped those round the tree too, which made it look rather nice. Tony threaded one or two short strings and let them hang down straight from a top bough.

'I say! It's looking fine,' he said, stepping back to see the tree. 'Uncle! Are you there? What do we do with the biscuits?'

Uncle Jack and Aunt Jane were in the other room dressing a tree for the children. Uncle Jack poked his head round the door. 'The biscuits?' he said. 'Why, thread a bit of cotton through one of the holes in each biscuit, tie a knot, and hang the biscuit up whole here and there on the tree – the birds will soon know how to deal with them!'

'Oh – so *that's* why we got biscuits with holes in them,' said Mollie. 'To thread through! Look – I'll get a needle and do the threading, Tony, and you can do the hanging.'

Soon the tree had eight or nine biscuits hanging on it. There was still room for something else, so they hung up some brazil-nuts too, and then Tony went to see if there was any bacon rind in the kitchen.

He came back with four long bits that Aunt Jane had put aside for the bird-table the next morning.

'We'll tie these on the tree instead,' he said. So they did. Then they looked at the little, straight green spike at the top of the tree and wondered what to put there.

'We can't put a fairy doll there,' said Mollie with a giggle.

'Let's put a bone!' said Tony. So they called to Aunt Jane, and she said they might go and take a nice bone from the veal bones in the larder. The butcher had brought them that morning for Aunt Jane to make soup from.

The children chose a nice meaty bone with plenty of fat on it. They tied it firmly to the top spike of the tree.

Uncle Jack and Aunt Jane came in to see their tree, and stood still in delight and surprise.

'You've done it beautifully!' said Uncle.

'It's the best one the birds have ever had,' said Aunt Jane. 'Oh, Jack – we'll give the children a few of our shiny tree-ornaments and silver-paper strings to hang on their tree. The birds won't take any notice of them – but it will make the tree look very quaint.'

So shiny, pink, green, yellow, and blue ornaments made of bright glass were hung on the tree too, and then the children carefully hung the long, narrow strips of tinfoil from many of the branches, to give the effect of icicles and frost.

The tree looked really beautiful. Everyone was very proud of it. The children wanted to put it on the bird-table at once, but Uncle said no, tomorrow was Christmas Day and both birds and children were to wait for their trees till then.

So, on Christmas Day, Tony and Mollie put their birds' Christmas tree outside on the bird-table. They carried it carefully. The birds sat on the roof and in the trees and looked at the strange and beautiful little tree in surprise.

Fresh water was put in the dish. A great slice of the maize-cake was put on the table. A large potato, baked in

its skin was also put there, and a scattering of sunflower-
and hemp-seeds.

'Merry Christmas, sparrows, robins, thrushes, blackbirds,
wagtails, and finches!' cried Mollie.

'Happy Day, blue-tits, coal-tits, great-tits, hedge-sparrows, and starlings!' called Tony. Then they both went
inside to look at their own presents.

But before they had even unwrapped a single one, Mollie caught sight of a bird on the Christmas tree! The birds
trusted the children so much that they felt sure the strange
tree was something good. So the robin had come down to
have a look at it

'See!' cried Mollie, 'he's sitting on the very, very top,
Uncle! He's better than a fairy doll. Look at him perching
there, as if he thought it was his very own tree!'

The robin opened his beak, swelled his red throat and
sang a very rich little tune.

'He's saying thank you!' said Tony.

Then down flew a streak of blue and yellow, a pretty
little blue-tit. He hung on to a piece of coconut and pecked
hard. Then came a great-tit and attacked the bone at the
top. The robin flew to a biscuit, and, sitting on the next
branch, pecked away daintily, enjoying the unusual treat
very much.

With a scurry of wings, and loud chirruping the bold
sparrows arrived. They pecked – with delight at the millet-
sprays. One smart little bird stayed on the table below,
pecking up the seeds that fell from the millet-sprays the
others were pulling at.

Soon the tree was full of birds. Starlings squabbled
about the bone and pushed each other off the tree.
Another robin arrived and sang angrily at the first one to
tell him to go. More tits came, and soon almost every nut

on the tree had its little blue and yellow bird, or a bold great-tit, peck-peck-pecking away.

The blackbird arrived, cocked his tail up and jumped up and down to get a biscuit. The thrush arrived, and, seeing the bird-cake untouched, rushed to get the currants from it. There was such a noise of chirrupping, tweeting, calling, and singing, and such a scurry and rush of wings!

'I could watch it all day,' said Tony in delight, quite forgetting his own presents.

'Other people are watching it too,' said Uncle Jack, nodding his head towards the hedge that ran alongside the lane. Sure enough, about a dozen people were there, peeping in surprise over the hedge at the birds in the Christmas tree.

'Do you mind them peeping, Uncle?' asked Mollie.

'Of course not!' said Uncle. 'I love them to see your tree -- maybe some of them will go home and do the same thing themselves. It would be fine if every family remembered the wild birds at Christmas time and gave them a treat.'

'Now come and undo your presents, children,' said Aunt Jane. 'You've got a few surprises!'

CHAPTER ELEVEN

Some Exciting Christmas Presents

THE children began to undo their presents. There was a big doll for Mollie from her mother, and a train for Tony. There was a doll's hairbrush and comb for Mollie from one of her aunts, and a small motor-car for Tony.

And from Aunt Jane and Uncle Jack there were presents that the children couldn't make out at all!

'What's this?' asked Tony, holding up what looked like a little wooden bell – but inside, instead of a clapper to ring, there was a small perch.

'That's a tit-bell,' said Uncle Jack.

'A tit-bell,' said Tony. 'What's that for?'

'We hang it up outside the window,' said Uncle Jack, 'but first we pour melted fat into it. When it is set hard we hang it up – and then you can watch the tits come and perch upside down on the little perch inside and peck away at the fat they love.'

'Oh, what fun!' said Tony, pleased. 'No other bird except the tits will be able to get at the fat, Uncle, because none of the others can swing upside down.'

'Quite right, Tony,' said Uncle Jack. 'And now what do you think this present of yours is, Mollie?'

'I don't know,' said Mollie, puzzled. She held up her present, which she had unwrapped.

'It has a top and bottom of wood, and a middle of tin, with slits in it,' said Mollie. 'What *can* it be for?'

Uncle Jack turned it upside down. There was a cork stuck in a hole underneath. Uncle Jack took it out.

'There,' he said, 'now you can fill the middle piece with shelled pea-nuts, from top to bottom. Put the cork in again, hang the peanut feeder outside — and the tits will come and swing on the feeder, pecking at the nuts through the slits as hard as they can, all day long.'

'Oh, that's a lovely idea!' cried Mollie. 'I shall shell pea-nuts today and fill the feeder. Then I shall cork it up and hang it outside. Thank you, Uncle Jack and Aunt Jane!'

'And now, what is this?' said Tony, opening yet another parcel, addressed both to him and to Mollie. 'Is it another sort of bird-feeder, Uncle?'

'Yes,' said Uncle Jack. 'This one is for the finches. It is rather like the peanut feeder, but the middle piece is made of glass, not tin. You fill it with seed. The seed trickles out at the bottom here, where these little grooves are in the wooden platform — do you see — so the birds can peck up as much as they want.'

'And the seed goes on trickling down as they peck it up, till the feeder is empty!' cried Mollie. '*That's* a good idea too!'

'Yes— "Eat what you may, but don't carry away!" is the rule for these peanut feeders and seed-hoppers,' said Aunt Jane, smiling. 'The nice part about them is that you can hang them as near the window as you like, for once the birds have found them they will come all day long and you can see the different kinds very closely indeed.'

'May we fill them and put them up now?' asked Mollie, who always liked to do things at once.

'Yes, if you like,' said Uncle Jack. 'Jane, will you melt some fat for us to pour into the tit-bell? We will be shelling the peanuts for the feeder.'

So they were all very busy the next half-hour, shelling the peanuts whilst the fat melted in the pan on the stove. Aunt Jane set the tit-bell upside down in a cup when the fat was ready. Then she poured the fat into the bell

'As soon as the fat is set hard, the bell will be ready to hang up,' she said. 'Next time we fill it we will mix minced-up peanuts with the fat – that will be an extra treat for the tits!'

'We'll fill the peanut feeder now,' said Uncle. He took out the cork at the bottom, and Mollie and Tony put the shelled nuts into the middle piece. They shook the nuts right down to the end, and then, when it was full, Uncle corked it up again.

'*That's* ready!' he said.

'Now for the seed-hopper,' said Mollie. 'I suppose it's called a hopper because the seeds hop out.'

The others laughed. 'You'll soon see how the seeds come out when it's filled,' said Uncle. He took out the long centre bolt that held the top, middle, and bottom together. He took off the top piece of wood, and then let the children fill the glass hopper from the top. They poured in the hemp-seed till it was full – then Uncle screwed it up.

'And *that's* ready too!' he said. 'This is the small size for gardens – but there is a bigger size for bird aviaries too. It is a useful thing for feeding birds because it needs no attention at all, except for filling when it is empty.'

'Now, can we hang them up?' asked Mollie, jumping up. 'Where shall we put them?'

'Well, now,' said Uncle, 'you can hang them in separate places, if you like – or you may hang them all together, one above the other – because, you see, each hopper, bell, and feeder has a hook at the top – and a metal loop underneath – so you can hook them all together, like this!'

Uncle Jack took the tit-bell, whose fat had now set. He took the seed-hopper and the peanut feeder and he hooked them all together – the seed-hopper at the top, the peanut feeder next, and the tit-bell at the bottom. 'There!' he said, 'what about hanging them up like that, one below the other, because then we shall see tits and finches and sparrows all day long, swinging together on our feeders!'

'That's a simply splendid idea!' cried the children, really delighted.

Uncle Jack took them outside. He hammered a big nail into the wooden top of the window, and then hooked the top of the seed-hopper to it. All the three bird-feeders then swung neatly out from the window-pane, ready for their feathered guests.

'Don't they look fine?' said Mollie. 'Will the birds come soon, Uncle?'

'We'll hang a bone under the tit-bell,' said Uncle Jack. 'The tits will see that and come to it – and then they will discover the fat inside and the peanuts above very quickly. We'll take the bone away when they've found the fat.'

So they hung a bone beneath the bell, and then went indoors.

In two minutes the tits had discovered the bone and had come darting down to it. In two seconds they found the fat inside the bell, and, with much calling and excitement, they began to peck at the fat they loved so much. Soon

there were half a dozen tits all waiting for their turn to hang upside down on the little perch.

Then two of them discovered the peanut feeder. They stood on the little wooden platform at the bottom of the feeder, and pecked with their tiny beaks through the slits at the peanuts. How busy they were!

Then, with a flurry and scurry of wings, down flew three sparrows to the seed-hopper and began to gobble up the seeds that trickled out, as fast as ever they could. More sparrows flew down, and soon, with the blue tits, coal-tits, and great-tits below, there were about sixteen birds fluttering and feeding just outside the dining-room window!

'This is simply lovely!' said Mollie. 'I could watch all day long. You *did* give us nice presents, Uncle!'

'It's a pity everyone can't buy things like these,' said Tony. 'People would so love to see the birds getting tamer and tamer.'

'Anyone who cannot afford these things can buy a small wire basket, which is very cheap,' said Aunt Jane. 'And they can fill it with all sorts of scraps, and hang it near their window. The birds will come and pull out whatever scrap they like the best.'

'*Our* birds are very lucky!' said Tony. 'They have a bird-table, a coconut, a peanut feeder, a seed-hopper, a tit-bell, and coconut shells and flower-pots to roost in!'

'And water to drink too!' said Uncle. 'Don't forget that – it's very important!'

CHAPTER TWELVE

The Bird that Plants Seeds

ONE wild morning after Christmas, the children looked out of the window and saw the trees swaying to and fro in a great wind.

'The poor little birds on the bird-table are almost blown away this morning,' said Tony. 'See how the wind fluffs their feathers the wrong way when they turn their backs to the wind.'

'Can you hear a bird singing in the storm?' asked Uncle Jack, coming up behind them.

Both the children had much sharper ears now and could hear the voices of birds very well indeed. They listened – and sure enough, in the song of the wind they could hear the voice of a bird – a bird that sang wildly and boldly, as if he were defying the storm.

'Can you hear him?' asked Aunt Jane. 'I can!'

'Yes – up at the top of that birch tree,' said Tony. 'It's a thrush. I can see his speckled breast. But he's a very big bird. Is it the thrush you called the storm-cock, Uncle?'

'Yes – it is,' said Uncle, pleased that Tony had remembered. 'Isn't his song lovely? So loud and ringing. He is called the mistle-thrush too – do you know why?'

'Does he like mistletoe?' asked Mollie, after thinking for a minute.

'You've guessed right!' said Uncle. 'Yes – he is very fond of mistletoe *berries*. He is quite greedy over them. And, do you know – he plants the seeds for the mistletoe!'

The children stared at Uncle Jack in surprise. 'You're joking!' said Tony. 'I didn't know any bird could plant seeds!'

'Well – shall we put some of our Christmas mistletoe out on the bird-table, with the green berries on it?' asked Uncle. 'Then we shall see the mistle-thrush closely, and perhaps I can show you later on how he plants the seeds. If it were not for the mistle-thrush and his fondness for the berries of the mistletoe, I am afraid no more mistletoe would grow in the woods!'

Well, of course, the very next thing the children did was to pull down the bunch of mistletoe that Aunt Jane had hung by the front door, and tie it to the twigs at the back of the bird-table!

Then back to their seat by the window they went, and waited. It wasn't very long before the mistle-thrush flew down. He looked at the berries with his head on one side, and then pecked them vigorously.

'He's much bigger than the song-thrush,' said Mollie. 'He looks quite a giant next to those sparrows! He is clumsier-looking than the other thrush, isn't he, Uncle – not so neat and tidy-looking. But he has plenty of freckles on his pale breast.'

'Look, Uncle – he is wiping his beak on the table-edge,' said Tony. 'Has he got something stuck to it?'

'Yes – he has!' said Uncle, with a laugh. 'The seeds in-

side the pearly berries of the mistletoe are very sticky.
They stick to his beak and he has to try and rub them off.
Now, watch! He has gone to that oak tree over there. Do
you see how he is rubbing his beak against that bough, trying his hardest to get the sticky seeds off? Well – he is
planting those seeds!'

The mistle-thrush

'But, Uncle – you can't plant seeds on a branch!' cried
Mollie.

'Yes, you can,' said Uncle, 'if they are mistletoe seeds.
Have you never seen mistletoe growing on a tree, children?'

'No,' they said, puzzled.

'Well, look high up in that oak tree at the bottom of the
garden,' said Uncle. 'Do you see that big fuzzy-wuzzy look-

ing bunch of stuff – rather as if someone had thrown a small bush into the tree and it had grown there? Well – that is mistletoe! It does not grow in the ground. It likes to send its roots down into the branch of a growing tree, so that it can use the sap of the tree for its own.'

'Oh, how strange!' said Mollie. 'Uncle, let's go out and see the branch the mistle-thrush has been standing on. I'd like to see if any seeds have stuck there.'

They put on their coats and went out. They went to the bough on which the thrush had been rubbing his beak – but there were no seeds there!

'Wait,' said Uncle, 'we must look *under* the bough! The seeds in their sticky juice trickle round the bough until they are below it, sheltered by the branch itself. Yes – here is a seed, look – and another!'

Sure enough, the children could see two small seeds from a mistletoe-berry sticking to the underside of the bough. They could even see the sticky little trail the seeds had made as they trickled slowly round the bough. Mollie touched a seed. It was very, very sticky – as sticky as glue. She went to the bird-table and squeezed a mistletoe-berry between her fingers. It was so very sticky that she could not get it off, however much she tried to wipe her fingers on a twig nearby, pretending she was a bird!

'The bird is clever – but the mistletoe is clever too, to make its seeds so sticky,' said Mollie, wiping her fingers on a handkerchief. 'What happens next, Uncle?'

'This tiny seed sends out a small root, or sinker, as we call it,' said Uncle. 'It pierces right down to the sap of the tree – the juice, you know – and then, with the food it gets from the sap, it builds up two tiny green leaves. Then more and more leaves grow – a flower comes – and that, in turn, makes berries for birds to eat and plant!'

'Uncle, will these seeds grow into mistletoe plants?' asked Tony.

'Quite likely,' said Uncle. 'We will press them very firmly into the bark – there – and later on in the year we will come and see if any leaves are growing, shall we? Then, in years to come, when the mistletoe bush is very big on this oak tree, I shall be able to pick my own mistletoe for Christmas, instead of buying it!'

'*I* shall plant mistletoe-berries on our trees at home,' said Tony. 'Then we shall have mistletoe too. Why, I suppose everyone could have mistletoe if they liked, Uncle! That is – if they knew the story of the mistle-thrush and how it plants seeds.'

'Tirra-lee, tirra-loo!' sang the mistle-thrush wildly, from the top of the tree. Another rain-storm was rushing up, and the trees were swinging to and fro as if a giant was shaking them.

'Quick! Come indoors before we get soaked,' said Uncle.

'Oh – can't we climb a tree and sit at the top in the wind and rain, and shout and sing too?' cried Mollie. 'I'd love to, Uncle, I'd simply love to! Let me be a storm-cock for once!'

'Certainly *not*!' said Uncle, and hurried them both indoors!

CHAPTER THIRTEEN

A Little Bird with a Big Voice

THE New Year came in, and the weather grew colder.

'It's funny,' said Mollie, shivering. 'The days are getting longer, but the winter seems to be getting colder instead of warmer.'

'Don't you know the old saying, Mollie?' asked Aunt Jane. 'As the days lengthen, so the cold strengthens.'

'Well, it's a true saying,' said Mollie. 'It's getting colder and colder.' She looked out of the window. 'Even the birds look cold, Aunt Jane. Do you see how fat they look? But it's because they puff out their feathers to keep them warm!'

'And that makes them look real little balls of fluff!' said Aunt Jane.

'How do their feathers keep them warm?' said Tony suddenly. 'There's no weight in a feather at all — I shouldn't have thought it would have kept anything warm!'

Uncle Jack knew the answer, of course. There really was nothing he didn't know about birds!

'Feathers don't keep the cold *out*,' he said. 'But they do keep the warmth *in*! A bird's body is very hot, and the feathers with their tiny, downy hairs will not allow the warmth of the bird's body to escape. They hold it *in* – close to the skin – so the bird is always warm!'

'I see,' said Mollie. 'How clever! That's what my woolly vest does, I suppose. It doesn't keep the cold out, but it does keep the warmth of my body in!'

'Listen,' said Tony, cocking up his head like a dog. 'There's a very big bird in the garden, I can hear!'

They all listened. A very loud song indeed came from somewhere in the garden. It went on for a little while and ended with a loud ringing call. Then another bird took up the song and answered, also very loudly, ending with exactly the same ringing notes.

'Good gracious! It's louder even than the mistle-thrush, I do believe!' said Mollie, in astonishment. 'It must be an awfully big bird, Uncle!'

'Well, as a matter of fact, it's a very *small* bird!' said Uncle, smiling. 'Very small, indeed. You haven't seen it on the bird-table yet, but you saw it roosting in the thatch.'

'Uncle! You don't mean the tiny wren, do you?' cried Tony, in surprise.

'Yes – the wren,' said Uncle. 'And look – it has flown on to the bird-table, just to show you what a little thing it is!'

The little brown wren had darted to the table, and had taken a quick look round at the food there. Another wren on the thatch sang loudly again, and the wren on the table opened its beak and answered, ending with the loud ringing call that seemed to be the wren's own particular song-ending.

'Yes,' said Mollie, 'it *was* the wren singing so loudly.

The wren is a small bird with a stumpy tail and a loud
voice

Uncle, what a very loud voice for so small a bird!'

'People are always astonished when they hear such a
tremendous voice coming from such a little thing,' said
Uncle Jack.

'I shall always know a wren when I see one because of his
funny, stumpy little tail,' said Mollie. 'I like him. He's a
dear little bird. We haven't seen a great deal of him,
Uncle? Is he shy – or rare?'

'Good gracious, no!' said Uncle. 'There are lots of wrens
about, and they are not in the least shy or timid. But as
they hunt for tiny insects under the hedges, behind the ivy,
and hidden places like that, we don't notice them as often
as we might. In fact, when some people see them scurrying
through the undergrowth, they think they are little brown
mice, not the little brown wrens!'

'It didn't eat much from our table,' said Mollie, disappointed.

'Well, it is *very* clever at finding little, hidden-away insects,' said Uncle Jack. 'And, unless the snow is deep on the ground, it does not come to the table as often as most birds. We shall see more of it if we get some snow. Now – that is one more bird to add to our list, children!'

Can you say them all? Mollie and Tony could!

CHAPTER FOURTEEN

Footmarks in the Snow

THE next week the north wind blew hard, and leaden-grey clouds gathered slowly in the north-east. The house was cold and dark, and Aunt Jane had to pile logs on to the fire, and light the lamps early.

'We'll get snow tonight,' said Uncle. 'The birds won't like that.'

'But *we* shall!' said Mollie, thinking joyfully of snow-balls and snowmen. 'Snow is great fun!'

Uncle Jack was right. Snow fell in the night, silently, slowly, and when the children awoke the next day there was a strange light shining from outside into their bed-rooms. They leapt out of bed and ran to the window.

'Oh – how beautiful!' cried Mollie. 'Everywhere is white! It's like magic!'

The dazzling snow reflected a white light into their rooms. Everything was changed and different. The trees stood perfectly still, their boughs covered with snow. The roofs of the cottages nearby were white. The grass was covered with a smooth, unbroken blanket.

'Quick! Let's get dressed and go out!' said Tony. So they washed, flung on their clothes, did their hair, cleaned their teeth, and rushed downstairs. Into the garden they went and danced along the path, their feet leaving footprints as they went!

'It's like Fairyland!' cried Mollie. 'And isn't everything still, Tony? It seems as if the garden is waiting for someone – or something. It's a lovely feeling.'

The snow began to fall gently again. The snowflakes floated down, large and feathery.

'They are like big goose-feathers,' said Mollie, catching some on her hand. They melted at once. 'Look up into the sky, Tony. It is a queer feeling to see so many thousands of snowflakes falling from the grey misty sky.'

They both looked up into the falling snow. Then they heard Aunt Jane tapping at the window.

'Come in to breakfast!' she called. 'Good gracious! Didn't you put your Wellington boots on? Naughty children!'

'Our feet aren't wet, Aunt Jane!' cried Mollie, stamping the snow off her shoes on to the mat. 'Uncle Jack! Look at the bird-table! We shall have to scrape the snow off it for the birds.'

'Yes,' said Uncle Jack. 'They will be pleased to have our peanut feeder and seed-hopper today. No snow is on those, for they are protected by the thatched roof above.'

After breakfast the children cleaned the snow from the bird-table and spread it again. They emptied the snowy water and put some more into the bowl. They shook the snow from the coconut. The birds sat in the bushes nearby and watched. They were longing for their breakfast.

'Poor things! They can't possibly find any insects or any seeds now,' said Tony. 'The snow has hidden everything!

They might be able to find a few berries – but that's all.
I'm glad we can feed them. I should hate to think of them
starving out here in the snow.'

'Uncle – look at our footprints in the snow,' said Mollie.
'Those are yours – the great big ones, Uncle! These are
mine, the smallest ones – and those are Tony's. And look –

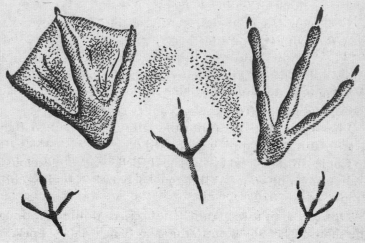

Some bird footprints. They are quite easy to see in
the snow

here is where Tony ran, because his footprints are a bit
farther apart, and deeper than when he walks.'

'What a lot you can tell from footprints, Mollie,' said
Uncle Jack. '*I* can tell something too. Look! Whose footprints are these?'

The children looked. They saw the marks made by the
two feet of a small bird. The feet were close together, and
made quite a little trail around the bird-table.

'It's a bird that hops,' said Mollie. 'You can tell that because its feet are close together in the prints. I expect it's a sparrow or a chaffinch.'

'Right, Mollie!' said Uncle Jack. 'Now here is the print of a bird with much bigger feet, look – and the feet are not together, but in a line, alternately. That means a big bird, that walks.'

'It's one of the fantail pigeons from next door,' said Tony. 'I saw one walking round the table this morning.'

'Come into the field behind my wood,' said Uncle. 'We may see some more prints there – interesting ones, too. Birds' feet are very different, you know.'

They went through the little gate that led from Uncle Jack's garden to the field. They hunted about for other prints – and they found plenty!

'Look here!' said Uncle. 'Here is an interesting one.'

The children looked down and saw, clearly marked in the snow, the three-toed foot of some small bird – but behind each footprint was another little mark in the snow, as if something on his foot had cut the snow each time he walked.

'That's the print of a lark,' said Uncle Jack. 'He has a long heel-claw growing at the back of each foot, so that he can steady himself as he runs through long grass – and the heel-claw shows clearly in his print.'

'Then there are are larks in this field,' said Tony. 'We shall hear them singing in the springtime!'

'Look, Uncle – here's another footprint,' said Mollie, stopping by the side of a small stream that ran through the field. 'Isn't it funny? It has three very big toes – and the print looks as if the toes are joined together with something!'

'It's a duck's footprint, silly!' cried Tony. 'Its feet are webbed, aren't they, Uncle?'

'Yes,' said his uncle. 'All the three toes are joined together with skin – and the web of skin shows in the snow-print. And do you see how the duck waddles?'

'Oh, yes!' said Mollie, looking closely at the footmarks. 'It turns its feet in very badly indeed – it went waddle-waddle-waddle all along by the side of the stream!'

'Look – here's a funny trail of footmarks!' said Tony suddenly. 'You can't tell which foot is which – because the trail is just one long single line, Uncle! Is it a bird with one foot?'

'No,' said Uncle, laughing. 'That's the print made by a moorhen, Tony. It is a big bird, as you can see by its foot-marks, and as it often makes its way through thick weeds and reeds, it has a habit of always putting one foot down exactly in front of the other, so as to get along easily. So its prints are in one long line, making it seem as if the bird had only one foot!'

'I didn't know that birds' feet were so different,' said Mollie, surprised. 'Why are they, Uncle? *Our* feet are all the same!'

'I'll tell you about that when we get home,' said Uncle. 'Come along, now – Aunt Jane will be wondering what has happened to us!'

CHAPTER FIFTEEN

All Sorts of Feet!

THEY were soon home. Aunt Jane was busy in the kitchen, so the children went to sit on the hearthrug in front of the lovely wood-fire that crackled so cheerfully and sent bright flames up the chimney.

Uncle Jack got a pencil, a rubber, and a writing-pad – his very biggest one.

'Oooh! – are you going to draw?' asked Tony, pleased.

'Yes,' said Uncle Jack. 'It is easier for you to see what I am talking about if I draw for you. Now then – you want to know why birds' feet are so different. Well, we know one set of feet very well, the feet of the birds that hop. Sparrows – chaffinches – robins – thrushes – starlings. And we know why they hop.'

'Yes – because they live in the trees and jump from twig to twig,' said Mollie, at once. 'And their feet are so used to jumping, that they go on jumping, or hopping, when they leave the trees and go to the ground!'

'Right!' said Uncle. He drew a little foot, with three toes in front and one behind. 'This is a chaffinch's foot,' said Uncle Jack. 'It has three jointed toes in front and one behind so that it can easily hold the twigs, and roost safely at night. It is the foot of a percher. A perching bird.'

'Now we'll have a swimming bird, Uncle,' said Mollie, 'I know it has webbed feet. Draw one!'

So Uncle Jack carefully drew the webbed foot of a duck – three toes, joined together with skin, and a small claw or spur behind.

'Swimming birds have webbed feet to help them to swim with, of course,' he said. 'They act like paddles or oars in the water – the bird *pushes* the water away with its webbed feet, the push sends it forward, and we say it is swimming along. It uses first one foot and then the other.'

'Why does a duck waddle so funnily on land?' asked Tony.

'It can't help it,' said Uncle Jack. 'Its feet grow so far back on its body, to help it in its swimming, that when it walks, it has to waddle.'

'Uncle, the moorhen is a water bird, isn't it!' said Mollie suddenly. 'But its feet are not webbed!'

'That is because it runs and walks a good deal, as well as swims,' said Uncle. 'It could not walk easily on land if it had webbed feet – but it finds it hard to swim fast with its unwebbed feet, Mollie. You must watch it next time you see it swimming, and you will see how it nods its head to and fro like clockwork, in its effort to swim along!'

'Oh, yes – I remember noticing that when I saw a moorhen on the lake in our park at home,' said Mollie.

Uncle Jack was drawing another foot. 'This is the foot of a climber – a climbing bird,' he said. 'What do you notice about it, children?'

'Why, it has two toes in front and two behind, as well,' said Mollie, at once. 'And I guess I know why! A climbing

Finch (percher)

Duck (swimmer)

Woodpecker (climber)

Partridge (scratching bird)

Eagle (bird of prey)

bird wants feet that won't slip easily when it climbs up the trunk of a tree – so it has the same number of toes behind as in front – and sharp, strong claws to help it too!'

'Mollie, you are really getting very clever,' said Uncle Jack, pleased. 'This is the foot of a woodpecker, who climbs along the trunks of trees all his life, searching for hidden insects. He needs well-balanced feet and strong claws – and he's got them! All climbing birds have the same sort of feet. Watch a tame parrot climbing about its cage and you will notice it has the same kind of feet.'

'Now draw some more, Uncle,' said Mollie. 'It's as good as doing a puzzle!'

Uncle Jack drew a strong, stout leg, rather short, with three very strong toes in front and one behind.

'It looks a bit like a hen's foot,' said Tony.

'You are nearly right,' said Uncle Jack. 'It belongs to a partridge – a scratching bird, like the hen. Scratching birds like to scratch in the ground for their food, so their legs are usually short and strong and their feet are strong, too. Their claws are often blunted with scratching. Hens scratch – and partridges, pheasants, and pigeons. Now let me see – that is four different kinds of feet, so far.'

'Yes – perchers, swimmers, climbers, and scratchers,' said Mollie, who had a very good memory. 'I shouldn't think there are any more, Uncle.'

'Oh, we've only done half!' said Uncle Jack, beginning to draw again. The children watched.

'Oh, Uncle – what a great, cruel-looking foot!' said Mollie. 'So strong – and with such awful claws. I shouldn't like to be caught in *that* foot!'

'That's what many little animals think,' said Uncle Jack. 'This is an eagle's foot. The eagle uses its feet to catch its prey in. It suddenly drops downwards on its small victim,

Plover (a wading bird)

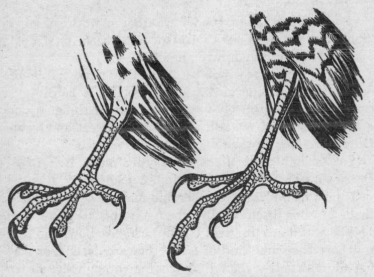

The kestrel and sparrow-hawk are birds of prey. Look
at their clawed feet

Moorhen (a swimming and walking bird)

and grips it tightly in its clawed foot. That is why it has such sharp, strong claws. We call this the foot of a bird of prey. It preys upon, or hunts, other creatures.'

'The owl does that, too, doesn't it,' said Tony.

'Yes – and the hawks,' said Uncle. 'They all have the same kind of feet, and often the legs of a bird of prey are feathered right to the toes, so that if a rat, for instance, should try to bite its captor's legs, the thick feathers protect it from the bite.'

'There are a lot of good ideas in the world of birds, aren't there,' said Tony. 'Oh, Uncle – what a tiny, weak-looking foot you are drawing now! Whose is it?'

'It's the foot of a swift, a bird that lives nearly all its life darting through the air,' said his uncle. 'It hardly ever comes to rest, and rarely uses its feet for anything. It does not perch or climb or walk – so its feet are weak and feeble. Do you see how all the four toes point forwards?'

'Yes,' said Mollie. 'It couldn't walk much if it tried! Doesn't it use its foot for anything, Uncle Jack?'

'It puts its four toes together and makes a sort of hook of them to hang itself up by when it wants to go to sleep against a wall or cliff,' said Uncle Jack. 'Swallows and martins have the same kind of feet – they are darters, or darting birds that live their lives darting through the air, instead of walking, perching, swimming, or climbing.'

Uncle Jack drew another foot with a long leg. 'This is the leg and foot of a wader,' he said. 'A wading bird, that wades in the water for its food. The heron does that, and the flamingo that you have seen at the Zoo, and the little plover. All of them have good long legs to raise them above the water, and their feet are flattened underneath to help them to wade on marshy ground.'

'There! Those are the different feet of the birds you

will see in our countryside,' said their uncle, showing them the whole page. 'Each foot tells a little tale of the bird's life, and says, "I am the foot of a bird that loves a tree-life!" or, "I am the foot of a bird who prefers the water!"'

'Uncle, what about the eighth sort of foot?' asked Mollie, counting the feet. 'You haven't done the eighth. Have you forgotten?'

'No,' said Uncle, 'but the eighth kind of foot isn't seen in our country, so I haven't drawn it. It would be the foot of a runner – a bird that runs more than it flies – a big bird, such as the ostrich or the emu. You've seen pictures of them, I expect. They have long, strong legs, and only two toes, short and thick, to help them to run fast. I won't draw them here, because we shan't see their feet as we go out walking in our countryside.'

'Draw the moorhen's foot instead,' said Mollie. 'That's a funny foot, I think, judging by the prints we saw in the snow this morning! That shall be the eighth foot, Uncle.'

So Uncle Jack drew the moorhen's foot for her – a large foot with very long toes – and then he pointed first to one picture and then another, saying, 'What bird does *that* foot belong to? What does *that* foot say?'

And do you know, Tony and Mollie got each one right! They knew all about the perchers, the swimmers, the climbers, the scratchers, the birds of prey, the darters, the waders, and the runners!

How many do *you* know? Cover up the names at the bottom of the pictures and see!

CHAPTER SIXTEEN

The Beaks Tell a Tale Too

THE next day there was more snow, and the children had to clear the bird-table well. The birds sat looking cold and hungry, and were very pleased indeed to see two warm potatoes that Aunt Jane had baked in their skins. They were given a good slice of the bird-cake too.

Mollie touched the string of peanuts, and found that they were nothing but shells! Every tiny bit of nut had been pecked out!

'Good gracious!' she said. 'The tits have eaten every peanut. We must thread some more for them. It's a good thing they have the peanut feeder to eat from.'

Tony looked up at the peanut feeder – and then he looked again. 'Mollie! The birds have eaten all the nuts from there too! Just fancy! We shall have to fill it again. There is plenty of seed in the seed-hopper, though.'

'And still half the fat left in the tit-bell,' said Mollie, looking up into it. 'I think we get all the birds of the countryside here now, Tony – they eat such a lot!'

They built a big snowman that morning and Aunt Jane gave them a funny old hat of Uncle Jack's for his head, and a scarf for his neck. The birds did not seem to mind him at all – except the fantail pigeons next door. They had been coming for seed now and again – but when they saw the snowman they flew off in alarm!

'Now you must really come in,' said Aunt Jane, seeing the children rubbing their hands in pain. 'The snow has chilled your hands. Don't get them warm too quickly, or you will be in great pain.'

Uncle Jack was reading by the fire, smoking his pipe. The children, their coats, hats, and boots put away, went to join him by the fire.

'Uncle! Do some more drawing for us, *please!*' begged Mollie. 'You are so good at it.'

'What shall I draw?' asked Uncle, putting down his book. 'Birds, I suppose!'

'Draw some different beaks,' said Tony. 'I expect they tell tales of what birds do and eat, just as the feet do.'

'Yes, they certainly do,' said Uncle. 'Now, where is that sheet of paper that I drew the feet on? Ah, here it is. Now – what shall I draw first? I'll draw one you know well!'

Head of a chaffinch

He drew the short, strong, cone-shaped beak and head of a small bird.

'Chaffinch!' cried Mollie. 'I know why he has a beak like that – because he is a seed-eater, and needs a very strong beak to husk seeds. I watched a sparrow yesterday trying to crack a big seed, to get at the kernel inside. He spat out the husk. Every day the table is full of the dry husks of seeds.'

'Yes – that is the beak of a seed-eater,' said Uncle Jack. 'You can always tell seed-eaters by their strong, short beaks. Now – here is quite a different kind of beak!'

He drew a tiny, thin little beak and a small head. The children looked at it in silence.

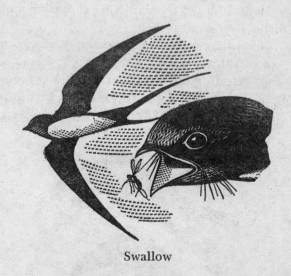

Swallow

'I don't know what bird that is,' said Mollie. 'I can only say that he doesn't eat seeds – but must eat something very soft and small.'

'You are right there,' said Uncle. 'It is the beak and head of a swallow, one of the insect-eating birds. You have seen the swallows flying high in the air in the summertime, hunting for insects. Birds that hunt insects on the wing have weak, short beaks, because they have no need to crack hard seeds, or peck at hard nuts. But they *do* need to be able to open their beaks very widely indeed, so that they may catch insects easily.'

'The robin eats insects, too, and so does the wren – and the blackbird and thrush,' said Tony. 'But they don't have weak, feeble beaks, Uncle. They have longer, thinner, beaks then the seed-eaters, I know – but they are not weak.'

'Ah, but such birds as the thrush and blackbird eat all kinds of things besides insects,' said Uncle. 'They need a stronger beak than the little swallow has, who eats *nothing* but insects on the wing. They have a sort of in-between beak – not so strong or so cone-shaped as the sparrow's – but not feeble like the swallow's.'

Uncle Jack began to draw a big, long beak, a head, and a

Heron

long neck. 'This is the beak of a heron,' he said. 'What does it tell you?'

'It's a fishing bird!' cried Tony. 'A bird that fishes for its food *must* have a long beak to reach the fish, and a sharp one to stab at it!'

Kingfisher

'Right,' said Uncle Jack. 'All fishing birds have long, sharp beaks like this. The kingfisher has one too. The heron has long legs that raise him above the water, and a long beak to reach the fish. The kingfisher does not need long legs, because he dives for his fish – but he needs a long, strong beak. In the spring I will take you to the lake and let you watch a kingfisher fishing.'

'Good,' said Tony. 'Go on drawing, Uncle. That is three beaks, so far – a seed-eater's beak, an insect-eater's beak, and a fishing-bird's beak. Draw another, and we'll guess what it is.'

Uncle Jack drew one that both the children guessed at

once. Can you guess it too? You will see it on this page.

'A duck! A duck!' they both cried. 'That's easy, Uncle.'

'Yes – it *is* easy,' said Uncle Jack, smiling. 'It is the beak of a diving bird. Diving birds need spoon-shaped beaks with holes in them, so that they may burrow and scrape about in the mud at the bottom of ponds and streams.'

Duck

'Why does a duck's beak have holes in it?' asked Mollie, puzzled.

'So that the water and mud can strain out of its beak, as it burrows,' said Uncle. 'The duck hunts for water-insects, filling its beak full of mud as it does so. The mud and water flow out of the holes in its beak – but the insects are left behind and swallowed!'

'Well, I didn't know *that* before,' said Tony, 'and I have watched the ducks on the pond in the park at home hundreds of times!'

'All diving birds have these strange beaks,' said Uncle Jack. 'They are flat and hollow, and are fringed with hairs. One of the funniest beaks is that of the spoonbill, which, like the duck, hunts in the mud for small water creatures. Its beak is exactly like two wooden spoons put together!'

'Draw another beak, Uncle,' begged Mollie. 'You *must* fill the page!'

Head of an eagle

Uncle Jack drew a big beak and head, and the children gazed at it, thinking it was a cruel beak.

'That cruel-looking beak matches the cruel-looking leg you drew before,' said Mollie suddenly. 'Is it a bird of prey's beak, Uncle?'

'Yes, it is,' said Uncle. 'This is an eagle's beak – and that was an eagle's leg. Flesh-eating birds have these hooked, pointed beaks, sharp and strong, which are used for tearing at their food. Hawks have beaks like this too. We call them carnivorous birds, or flesh-eaters – or birds of prey, as you already know.'

'You've got room for one more beak,' said Mollie. 'Just

there, in the right-hand top corner. Draw a big, funny beak, Uncle.'

So her uncle began drawing again – and it certainly *was* a curious-looking beak.

'This bird has a big beak, and underneath is a pocket,' said Uncle Jack. 'It uses this pocket to store fish in. The pocket is made of very elastic skin, that can stretch tremendously. When it is full of fish it looks like a market-bag full of goods! What bird is it?'

'A pelican!' cried Mollie. 'I've seen one at the Zoo. Its pocket-beak was full, and it *did* look funny!'

'Well, there you are,' said Uncle, putting the drawing

Pelican

into Mollie's hand. 'A sheet of beaks and feet! And they each tell a tale about a bird's ways. Whenever you see a bird, look at it well, beaks and feet and all – and see what you can guess about its habits.'

'Thank you!' said Mollie, taking the drawings in delight. 'You've drawn eight legs and six beaks.'

'The beaks of a seed-eating bird, an insect-eater, a fishing bird, a diving bird, a flesh-eater – and a bird with a pocket-beak!' said Tony. 'I know them all. Do you, Mollie?'

'Of *course*!' said his sister. And she did!

Bird-table

CHAPTER SEVENTEEN

What the Birds Say

THE snow melted away. The warm winds came, and the garden grew green again. It was the beginning of February.

One morning Mollie woke up early. Some sparrows were chirruping loudly outside, and she listened to them. Then she heard a great chorus of many other birds. They all sang and sang. She tried to pick out their songs and pretty calls, but she couldn't.

'I simply don't know which bird is singing which song!' she said, quite crossly. 'Now Uncle could lie here and say "Ah – that's a blackbird! Oh, that's a chaffinch – and there's a tit." But all *I* can say is "I hear the sparrows chirruping, but the other songs are just a great big lovely noise." I *wish* I knew which was which.'

Mollie told Uncle all this at breakfast-time, and he laughed. 'A great big lovely noise!' he said. 'Yes, you are right, it is. And separating out that great big lovely noise into its different single songs is just as interesting as listening to a band, and trying to make out the different instruments – the piano, the violin, the 'cello, and the rest.'

'Well, Uncle, can't you help us?' asked Tony, who had also heard the noise that morning.

'Of course,' said Uncle. 'And this is a splendid time of year to learn the bird notes and calls, because in the springtime every bird is happy, and is singing gaily and loudly. I'll take you out into the garden after tea and we'll listen to the birds' goodnight songs. They are nearly as beautiful as their morning chorus.'

So that evening the children went into the garden in the golden light of the sinking sun, and listened.

'Now do you see that bird up in the top of the ash tree?' asked Uncle. 'He is singing loudly.'

'The blackbird?' said Mollie. 'Yes.'

'Now listen to him,' said Uncle. 'Most people can't tell the difference between a thrush singing and a blackbird. I shall be proud if *you* can!'

They all listened to the blackbird. He sang slowly and beautifully, and his song was pure and liquid. He seemed really to sing a melody, and he went on and on and on, hardly ever repeating himself.

'He really seems to me to be thinking of what he is singing, and to be listening to the tune himself,' said Mollie, pleased.

'Yes, he does. But listen when he comes to the end of his tune,' said Uncle. 'He will probably make a horrid noise – a kind of explosion or hiss.'

He did! The children laughed. Then the blackbird began his song again, loud, clear, mellow – and once more ended weakly with a horrid noise.

'His voice is like a flute,' said Tony.

'Yes,' said Uncle. 'And now listen closely, please. Our

song-thrush is over there – see – in the birch tree. What do you notice about his song?'

'Ju-dy, Judy-Judy!' sang the thrush, in a clear voice very like the blackbird's. 'Mind how you do it! Mind how you do it! Pretty-boy, pretty-boy, pretty-boy! Coo-ee-oo! Coo-ee-oo! Jug-jug-jug!'

'Yes – he's lovely too,' said Mollie. 'But what I notice about *his* song is – he repeats his little sentences. The blackbird doesn't repeat himself, he goes on and on. But the thrush keeps saying things two or three times over.'

'Your ears are getting as good as mine, Mollie,' said Uncle Jack, very pleased. 'That's just how you can tell a thrush from a blackbird at once, when they are singing. Their tone is different too – but some thrushes are much better singers than others, and might easily be mistaken for a blackbird or even a nightingale.'

'Quick, Uncle – there's our chaffinch on the hedge,' said Tony. 'And *he's* singing too – loudly and cheerfully! And now there's another answering him. And another somewhere in the distance. The song is the same each time. It's sweet. Don't they all rattle it out?'

'The chaffinches have been practising the last week or two,' said Uncle. 'Their song always sounds to me like this – "chip – chip – chip, cherry-erry-erry, chippy-you-EE-ar!"'

'Chip – chip – chip, cherry-erry-erry, chippy-you-EE-ar!' repeated Mollie.

'Whisper it,' said Uncle. 'It sounds more like the song then.' So Mollie whispered it. 'Chip – chip – chip, cherry-erry-erry, chippy-you-EE-ar!'

And a chaffinch nearby looked at her and cried loudly, 'chip – chip – chip, cherry-erry-erry, chippy-you-EE-ar!' That made them all laugh.

'Uncle, that's just like the chaffinch's song,' said Mollie, whispering the words again.

'Most chaffinches begin their song with a loud "chip – chip – chip!"' said her uncle, 'and they love to end it with a little rattling cry of "chippy-you-EE-ar!" It is easy to hear when once you have really learnt it. We shall hear the chaffinches carolling loudly now, all over the garden. You will soon know their song very well indeed.'

'Look, there's a starling on our chimney,' said Tony. 'Is *he* going to sing too?'

'Well – I expect he'll try to, poor chap,' said Uncle. 'It won't be much good though. Starlings do their best to sing, but they never can. Listen to that fellow up there now – he's just beginning.'

The starling opened his bright yellow beak and swelled his throat. But no beautiful song came.

'Wheeze, splutter, click-click, skeeze, skeeeeeze, kick-kick, eeee, click!' sang the starling, making a most extra-ordinary collection of noises. The children laughed at him. But he went on and on trying.

'He probably thinks he is singing marvellously,' said Uncle Jack. 'Well, he is an excellent imitator, if he isn't a good singer. I once heard a starling imitating the noise of the ice-cream man's bell so well, that I kept running out to see if the ice-cream man was there. And then I found that it was a starling on the roof, making the bell-noise again and again!'

'I wish I could hear that,' said Tony. 'Look – a chaffinch again. Is he going to sing?'

The chaffinch didn't sing his song. He flew to the bird-table, and said 'pink, pink!' very loudly indeed. 'Pink, pink!'

'Oh – he said "pink pink!" then and didn't sing the song you told us,' said Mollie.

'Birds sing songs, and have call-notes and alarm-notes too,' said Uncle. 'That is the chaffinch's call-note. He always says "pink pink!" loudly. Because of that, some countryfolk call him the spink. Now listen – what is *that* bird?'

They listened, and heard a loud song with a bold, ringing ending. 'The wren,' said Mollie. 'I'd know that loud vigorous song anywhere!'

'Good,' said Uncle. 'And now listen to one more singer – the robin. He is always the last to bed, and although it is now getting dark, he will sing just one more song before he goes to roost.'

So they listened to the robin's short, rich song, very creamy and sweet. Then, as he spied a cat in the distance, stalking down the lane, his song stopped and he began to cry 'tick-tick-tick!' very loudly indeed.

'His alarm-note,' said Uncle.

'It's like a big clock being wound up,' said Mollie.

'It is,' said Uncle. 'Now you've heard songs, call-notes, and alarm-notes. And, if my ears are right, there's your aunt's call-note too. Listen!'

It was. 'Jack! Tony! Mollie! Whatever are you doing out there? It's getting dark and cold. Come in at once!'

'The call-note of mothers and aunts,' said Tony solemnly, and they all went indoors laughing.

CHAPTER EIGHTEEN

A Few More Songs

THE children soon knew the songs of all the birds they had
listened to with Uncle Jack. They began to listen hard by
themselves each day, and soon found it quite easy to find
out which bird was singing.

'I've learnt the wagtail's call, that you told us before
Christmas,' said Tony to his uncle. 'He says "chissic, chissic!" and he has a bright, sweet little warbling song.'

'Yes – he has,' said his uncle. 'And the hedge-sparrow has
a dear little song now, too – have you heard him yet? It is
rather high, and he sings it as if he is insisting on something. I heard him yesterday.'

'We'll listen,' promised Mollie. 'What about the tits,
Uncle? They are calling all over the garden now, and I *do*
find it so difficult to make out which is which.'

'Well – there are the three different kinds outside the
window just now,' said Uncle. 'We'll listen and see what
they each say. Ah – did you hear that?'

'Pink, pink!' said the great-tit loudly. 'Pink, pink!'

'That's what the chaffinch says,' said Mollie.

'The great-tit says it too,' said her uncle. 'Now listen to him. He has gone to that tree – and he is calling "tea-cher, tea-cher, tea-cher, teach!" Isn't it a funny up-and-down song?'

'It sounds like somebody sharpening a saw or something,' said Tony.

'How queer you should say that,' said Uncle Jack. 'People often call him the saw-sharpener!'

'Now the blue-tit is saying something,' said Mollie. 'Listen! He is tinkling it out merrily.'

'Pim-im-im-im-im! Pim im-im-im-im!' sang the little blue-tit in a tinkling voice. Then, as another tit flew to his coconut, he churred angrily, raising up a little blue crest of feathers on his head. 'Tee-tee-tee-tee!' he scolded.

'Pim-im-im-im-im,' and 'tee-tee-tee-tee!' said Mollie. 'Thank you, blue-tit – we know what *you* say now!'

And, as if the coal-tit wanted her to hear *his* voice too, he called out loudly from the peanut feeder. 'If-he, if he, if-he, if-he!'

'Good,' said Tony. 'We've heard you all now, and we'll listen again and again. Soon we shall be able to say, just as Uncle does, "Ah! Did you hear that coal-tit calling?" "Oho, there's a chaffinch carolling merrily in the garden!" "Dear me, there's the wren again, with his loud voice!" "Ah, I can hear the starling clucking and clicking on the chimney!"'

Uncle Jack laughed and tried to pull Tony's nose. 'You are cheeky,' he said. 'I'll pull your beak, and make *you* sound your alarm-note!'

But he couldn't catch Tony. 'I haven't got wings, but my legs are as good as a running bird's!' he shouted, as he tore to the bottom of the garden.

Mollie slipped her arm into her uncle's. 'I'm awfully

pleased you've taught us such a lot,' she said. 'I feel proud to think I know so many garden birds now, Uncle, and can even tell their songs.'

'There are many more to learn,' said her uncle. 'But once you've learnt a few, it is easy to hear and learn the others. You are both getting very good indeed!'

CHAPTER NINETEEN

Nesting-Time – and Nesting-Boxes

ONE fine, warm spring day Uncle Jack took down the bird-table. The children were very sad, but Uncle was firm about it.

'No,' he said, 'no more bird-table! We have fed the birds well all the winter, and now they must work for their living, and give *us* a bit of help! There are plenty of insects about, and I see greenfly on my rose-ramblers already. The birds must help me by clearing them away. If I feed them now, they will not work for themselves and their young ones.'

So down came the bird-table; and the seed-hopper and feeder were no longer filled. Mollie and Tony felt quite lost with nothing to do.

'What can we do for the birds now?' they asked.

'Well, you can still put down water for them to bathe in,' said Uncle. 'And, if you like, we'll go and buy two nesting-boxes, one for each of you. You can each choose a place to hang them, and we will see if the tits nest there.'

'Oh, how lovely!' cried Mollie. 'I'd like that.' She and

Tony and Uncle Jack went to buy the boxes that very day. There were nice ones, made out of bored logs, with the bark left on, and others, just plain boxes with a lid that jutted over the nesting-hole to protect it.

All the boxes had lids or roofs that lifted up so that the children could see when a nest was begun. Each had a small hole near the top for the birds to enter by.

Mollie chose a box made from a log, and the roof of it was a bit of wood with the bark still on. Tony chose the other kind of box. They took them home proudly.

'Nesting-boxes must be rain-proof, and must be as near the usual colour of tree-trunks as possible,' said Uncle Jack. 'They must look *natural* to the birds, who will be scared of anything that looks unusual. Now – where shall we put them?'

'High up in the ash tree?' suggested Tony, without thinking.

'Oh – I suppose you are thinking of climbing up to the top every day to see if the birds are nesting in your box?' said Uncle Jack.

Tony laughed. 'No,' he said. 'That was silly of me. I must put my box somewhere low enough for me to look into, of course.'

'Yes – and you must choose somewhere shaded, but not too dark, and you must not place your box facing to the south,' said Uncle. 'Birds do not like great heat on their nest.'

Mollie soon found a good place for hers. She put it against a big post up which grew a rose-rambler, thick and green. The rambler shaded the box, but did not make it too dark and airless. Tony chose a birch tree trunk for his box, and put it there, shaded by some nearby greenery. Both children lifted up the lids of their boxes and peeped

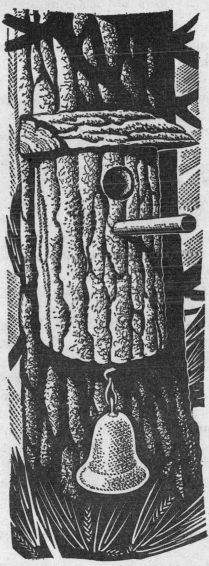

A tit nesting-box with a tit-bell below to attract the tits

inside. They were quite empty, of course, but how they hoped that one day they would be full of baby birds!

Tony nailed a little perch to the front of his box – and Mollie had such a good idea. She took the tit-bell, which still had some fat in it, and hung it up under her nesting-box.

'Now the tits will come there for the fat, and see my box, and nest in it,' she said.

'Oh! I do wish *I* had a tit-bell too,' said Tony, looking quite gloomy.

'A bone will do just as well,' said Uncle, 'Hang one up beneath your box, and the tits will visit that too.'

So Tony hung up a big bone – and Uncle Jack was perfectly right – the tits found it at once. They went to the tit-bell too, under Mollie's box, and soon the two children were in a state of great excitement, feeling quite certain that the birds were going to nest at once.

The starlings found Tony's bone too, and one starling poked his head inside the hole of the box, and then began to talk about nesting there.

'Oh – I want tits, not starlings!' cried Tony.

'Don't worry,' said Uncle. 'The hole is too small for the starlings. They will just argue with the tits, and then fly off when they find they can't really use the box.'

There was a fine quarrel. The tits shouted angrily at the starlings, and the starlings called the tits all the rude names they knew, which was quite a lot. But at last the bigger birds flew away, and the tits decided to take the box for themselves.

'They are great-tits,' said Tony happily. 'Aren't I lucky, Uncle?'

'I think Mollie is going to be lucky too,' said Aunt Jane. 'I can see see two blue-tits on her box!'

Starlings and tits

Well, it wasn't long before the blue-tits and the great-tits made their nests in the two boxes – and to Uncle Jack's great delight a pair of coal-tits chose an empty coconut shell to nest in as well!

The children watched the birds. They made their nests of bits of moss, grass, and hair, bringing in the pieces all day long. Uncle Jack allowed the children to lift up the roofs each day and peep inside, so that they could see exactly how the nests were getting on.

'I haven't seen you lift up the roof on your coconut yet, to see how your coal-tits are getting on, Uncle,' said Tony slyly.

'I'll squash you inside the coconut and make you look there for yourself,' said Uncle Jack. Tony laughed. He was sure his birds would finish their nest first, and he was pleased.

The nests were soon made. One day when Mollie was peeping at hers, she said, 'How does the nest get that pretty cup-shape, Uncle? It didn't look to me as if the birds were trying to make it that shape, when they brought the bits in.'

'The birds make it that shape by getting on to the nest, and working their little bodies round and round in it,' said Uncle. 'It is just the shape and size of their small bodies – and very comfortable it is, too!'

'Are there other nesting-boxes besides these?' asked Mollie.

'Oh, yes,' said Uncle. 'There are open-fronted ones for robins to build in, and there are special boxes made for owls, woodpeckers, and others. We will try those another year.'

The next great excitement was the laying of eggs. The great-tit laid hers first, then the blue-tit, and then the coal-tit. Tony gave a shriek of delight when he lifted up the roof gently one morning and found a white egg, marked with a few reddish spots, in the little nest.

A robin's nesting-box with an open front

'The first egg!' he said.

'Yes – and it's likely to be the last if you shriek like that,' said Uncle Jack. 'You will have to be extra careful now, in looking into the box, or you may make the birds desert their eggs.'

Mollie found a white egg, dotted with pale red-brown, in her box, and inside Uncle's coconut was another red-spotted white egg! All the hen tits had begun to lay.

The great-tit laid six eggs in Tony's nesting-box. The blue-tit laid eight for Mollie, and inside the coconut shell the coal-tit laid seven. The children were simply delighted.

'Twenty one new tits for the garden in the summer, Uncle!' cried Mollie.

The hen birds sat close on their nests each day now, and the cocks brought food to them – greenfly, grubs, and caterpillars of all kinds. If Mollie looked in at her blue-tit, it hissed at her, and pretended to peck.

'Don't be afraid, little bird,' said Mollie. 'I won't hurt you!'

Coal-tits' babies in the coconut shell

Another great day was when the eggs began to hatch out into queer, tiny babies, ugly and blind. The children could hardly believe they would ever grow into pretty, feathered birds.

But day by day they grew and altered – their downy feathers came, and it was not long before there were a great many fluffy yellow babies in each nest.

Then how busy the parent-birds were all day long, bringing food to their twenty-one children! The rose-ramblers were stripped of their greenfly. The caterpillars disappeared. The flies that danced in the morning and evening sun were caught by the hundred. In their sharp beaks the six tits took hundreds of insects to their young ones.

'Now you can see what a great deal of good is done by the birds in the springtime,' said Uncle Jack. 'Without them our plants would be ruined, our crops destroyed, our trees stripped of their leaves. They do peck at our fruit-buds sometimes, it is true, to find grubs there; and they do spoil some of our peas and our autumn fruit – but they do far more good than harm.'

One day the blue-tit took her young ones from the nest. They sat on a nearby twig in a row; fluffy yellow babies as sweet as anything could be. Mollie was overjoyed. To think they had grown up in her nesting-box!

Soon the garden was full of tiny tits being taught to fly and to feed themselves. The children loved them and watched them eagerly.

'Why don't more people put up nesting-boxes and bird-tables?' wondered Mollie. 'We've had more fun and pleasure out of Uncle's garden birds than we've had out of any toy!'

The nesting-boxes were not empty and cold when the

young ones had flown – because the tits went back there each night to roost! The children saw them there one night when they went to look with their torch.

They lifted up the roof – and cuddled inside was a crowd of tits, fluffy, cosy, and snug – a happy little family together!

CHAPTER TWENTY

The Lucky-Bag

'UNCLE JACK, all the birds are building their nests now,' said Mollie, one day. 'Do they all build them of the same stuff as the tits used?'

'Oh, no,' said Uncle Jack. 'Different birds use different things, Mollie. Big birds, such as the rooks, use quite long, strong twigs for their large nests. The blackbird uses small twigs, besides roots and fibres, and lines his nest with mud, and puts a soft lining of grass over the mud. The thrush builds the same kind of nest but doesn't bother to cover his mud lining.'

'What else do the birds use?' asked Tony. 'I saw a sparrow with a feather in its beak yesterday.'

'Birds use anything they can find that will make a good nest and a soft lining,' said Uncle Jack. 'Moss, dead leaves, grass, wool, hair, feathers, fur – anything that is handy and usable. But if you want to know what each bird really likes, why not hang up a lucky-bag?'

'Whatever's that?' asked Mollie.

'It's a net bag which you can stuff with all kinds of

Birds love a lucky-bag, full of odds and ends which
they may pull out and use for their nests

nesting-materials,' said Uncle Jack. 'I'll get one of Aunt Jane's old ones and then we'll stuff it full.'

So, with one of Aunt Jane's net shopping-bags, the children wandered out to the fields with Uncle Jack to find nesting-material.

'Here are some nice dry oak-leaves,' said Tony, stuffing them into the bag.

'And here is some old dry moss,' said Mollie.

'There are some clumps of sheep-wool caught on the black-berry brambles over there,' said Uncle Jack. 'Put some in – and look, here are some feathers from a bird killed by a fox – partridge feathers.'

Into the bag they all went. When it was almost full they went home again. Aunt Jane was emptying her carpet-sweeper, and Mollie pounced on the fluff that came out of it at once. 'Just the thing!' she said. 'Oh, and Uncle – would they like the hairs out of my hair-brush, do you think?'

'Sure to,' said Uncle. So Mollie combed her brush well, and stuffed the brown hairs from it through the holes of the lucky-bag.

'There!' she said. 'The lucky-bag is quite, quite full! What do we do with it now, Uncle?'

'We'll hang it up somewhere,' said Uncle Jack. So they hung it from a bush near the window – and it was not long before dozens of birds discovered it.

How carefully they examined that bag to see what they could take from it to help in the building of their nests! The robin dragged out the dead leaves. The sparrows went off with the feathers and fluff, and some hay that Tony had pushed in. The wagtail took some hairs and the hedge-sparrow was excited to find the sheep's wool.

Each of them flew off with their treasure in their beaks,

and, by watching to see where they went, the children guessed where to look for their nests!

'Yes,' said Uncle Jack, 'a lucky-bag is a great help in discovering not only what birds like for their nests – but where they are building them! Every bird flies straight to its nest when it has something to tuck into it. We must have a hunt around and see whose nests we can find.'

The children stuffed all kinds of things into their lucky-bag, as the birds began to empty it. They put some bits of Aunt Jane's mending-wool, strips of raffia from the garden-shed, pieces of tissue paper – anything they could think of!

The robin took the raffia. The tits took the wool, and the chaffinch flew off with the tissue paper! 'And now,' said Mollie, 'it's about time we saw the nests that *we* have helped to build, Uncle. Come along!'

CHAPTER TWENTY-ONE

The Nests in the Garden

UNCLE JACK knew of many nests in the garden. 'Oh, why didn't you tell us about them?' asked Tony. 'We would have loved to see them, Uncle!'

'I didn't want to have you poking round the new nests whilst the birds were laying their eggs,' said Uncle. 'A bird will easily desert its eggs, you know, if it is frightened. Then they grow cold, and will not hatch.'

'But, Uncle, we have learnt now to be very quiet when we go round looking for things,' said Mollie. 'I never make quick, sudden movements now, do I? And we both talk very quietly, Tony and I – we don't squeal and shout any more.'

'Yes, that's true,' said Aunt Jane, who was listening. 'The children are real bird-lovers now, Jack. Show them a few nests!'

'Very well,' said Uncle Jack. 'Come along. I'll show you one of the most beautiful sights in the world – and it is in my garden!'

The children followed him. He took them to a hawthorn

hedge that ran round the garden. It was just breaking into leaf. A small bird flew out of the hedge as they came near.

'The hedge-sparrow!' said Mollie, knowing him at a glance now. 'Is it his nest, Uncle?'

'It is,' said Uncle Jack. 'Look!' He parted the twigs, and the children peeped between them. They saw a little nest

Cluster of hedge-sparrow eggs

made of twigs, grass, and moss, beautifully lined with hair and wool. And inside the nest were four of the prettiest eggs the children had ever seen.

'Uncle! They are as blue as the sky!' cried Mollie in delight. 'What a marvellous colour!'

'It's beautiful,' said Tony, gazing at the brown nest and the cluster of blue eggs in the cup. 'To think that the little, dull-brown hedge-sparrow should lay eggs that colour. I never saw such a perfect blue!'

'Well, I am glad you think it's a lovely sight,' said Uncle Jack, pleased. 'Look – here is an old nest, made by a thrush last year, hidden in this same hedge. We'll take it out and have a look at it.'

He pulled it out. The children looked at it eagerly. It was made of root-fibres, grass, moss, and dead leaves, all interwoven very cleverly. Mollie pulled a long piece of grass out.

'Uncle, look – that long bit of grass was woven in and out almost half round the nest,' she said. 'How could the thrush weave it in and out like that? He hasn't any hands. Does he use his feet?'

'No,' said Uncle Jack. 'He only uses his beak – and with his clever beak he weaves this marvellous nest, making it strong, light, and comfortable. Birds use nothing but their beak when making their nests.'

'Who teaches them how to do it?' asked Mollie, puzzled.

'Nobody,' said Uncle, laughing. 'Every bird is born with this knowledge of how to make its own nest, and when the right time comes, it knows, without being told, that it must look for twigs, leaves, moss, and so on, and must find a good place, and weave there a strong little nest for eggs.'

'It's like magic,' said Mollie.

'It is, rather,' said Uncle Jack. 'It's a sort of magic that we call "instinct". You will find this magic all over the world, in birds, insects, animals, and even in ourselves. Butterflies use this magic when they want to lay their eggs – because, although they do not know that hungry caterpillars will come from their eggs, they seek and find exactly the right leaves to put their eggs on – so that the caterpillars may find food as soon as they hatch. The butterflies find the right plant by "instinct", you see.'

'Do spiders have that magic instinct too?' asked Tony.

'Of course!' said Uncle. 'No one teaches them how to make their marvellous webs. Instinct comes to their help, and by its magic they find themselves able to weave webs in the most perfect way.'

'This thrush's nest has a mud lining,' said Tony, looking at it again.

'Yes,' said Uncle. 'And, as I told you before, the blackbird, whose nest is very like the thrush's, adds grass to his mud lining. Look – there is an old blackbird's nest in that tree. I'll get it.'

The children looked at the old nests and saw that the blackbird *had* added a neat grass lining. 'Now I shall always know the difference between the two nests,' said Tony, pleased.

'Where does the robin nest?' asked Mollie, looking round. 'He is such a friendly little bird that I should have thought he would build near the house.'

'He loves to build in something that once belonged to us, his friends,' said Uncle. 'He will build in old boots in the ditch, old saucepans, tins, kettles – anything like that.'

'What funny places to choose!' said Mollie. 'What has *our* robin chosen, Uncle?'

'I'll show you,' said Uncle Jack, and he led them to the bottom of the garden. He kept his roller there – and do you know, inside the roller, the robin had built his nest!

'What do you think of that!' said Uncle, as the children bent down to look inside the big roller. 'I haven't been able to roll my grass for ages – because the robin has made it his home!'

The hen robin was sitting close on her grey-brown eggs. She did not move, but looked at the children with her bright black eye. Her nest was untidy – dead leaves, moss, and hay spread out from it, but it looked very comfortable.

'I suppose she has made her nest just the same cup-shape as all nests are?' asked Mollie.

'Just the same,' said Uncle Jack. 'All birds get into their nests and work their little bodies round and round to make them a comfortable cup-shape. Then the eggs will not fall out.'

'I know where the sparrows have built!' said Mollie, and she pointed up to where a pipe came down from the eaves of the house. 'Just behind that pipe, Uncle.'

'Yes,' said her uncle. 'Sparrows often build somewhere about the house – untidy little things they are, too. Just look at those long wisps of hay hanging down by the pipe. Why don't the lazy little birds tuck them in neatly!'

The children laughed. 'It seems as if the birds are like children, Uncle – some neat and tidy, and some untidy!' said Tony.

The chaffinch builds a neat, pretty nest

'Now I'll show you the chaffinch's nest,' said Uncle Jack. He took them to an apple tree, and there, in the fork between the trunk and a branch, was a small, very neat nest.

'Isn't it beautifully made!' cried Mollie. 'Moss, wool, hair – all closely pressed together – and lined with feathers from our lucky-bag – and, oh *look*, Tony! It's got some hairs from my hair-brush! Uncle, those are my own hairs there.'

It really was a nice feeling to think that the chaffinch's pretty eggs were lying closely on hairs grown on Mollie's own head. Mollie felt as if she had helped to make the nest. She looked at it closely.

'Look – the chaffinch has decorated its nest outside with scraps of white bark!' said Mollie, in surprise. 'Did it do it on purpose?'

'Oh, yes,' said Uncle Jack. 'The chaffinch loves to make its nest pretty. Once there was a chaffinch who built its nest in a yew bush near a church door – and it decorated its nest with the bits of confetti-paper it picked up from the path!'

'How odd its nest must have looked!' cried Tony.

'It did,' said his uncle. 'And now for our last nest – the wren's.'

'I know! In a hole in the thatch!' cried Mollie. 'I've seen him going in and out.'

So Mollie showed the nest – and then Uncle Jack showed her two more wren's nests at the back of the house. In each nest was a bright-eyed mother wren, sitting on four or five tiny eggs.

'You remember I told you what a lot of nests the wren makes before he decides on one?' asked Uncle Jack. 'All these nesting-holes here – three, four, five, eight, nine – look, ever so many – have been made by the wren. But when he picks the one for his eggs, he lines it cosily with hair and feathers and moss and then sticks to that one.'

'Well, I *do* know something about nests now,' said Mollie, pleased. 'What a lot of places nests are built in, Uncle. Holes, hedges, trees, thatch – and garden-rollers!'

CHAPTER TWENTY-TWO

A Bit about Eggs

'WHY are eggs the shape they are?' asked Tony, when they had gone indoors again. 'Why are they *oval*, Uncle?'

'I'll show you,' said Uncle. 'Go and ask your aunt for four new-laid eggs.' So Aunt Jane was begged for four hen's eggs. She gave them to the children, and they took them to the dining-room. Uncle had made a sort of nest out of a small rug. He took the eggs and put them into the cosy hole. 'Now look,' he said, 'if I put the eggs with their small ends pointing to the middle, see how cosily they all fit together, and how little room they take.'

'Oh, yes,' said Mollie. 'I can see that if a bird had big eggs, or a great many, to sit on, she would have to pack them into as small a space as possible, or some would be left out in the cold! After all, she isn't big enough to cover a large number of eggs, unless they are packed well together.'

'Quite right, as usual, Mollie,' said Uncle Jack. 'And there is another reason for the oval shape, too – especially when eggs are much thinner at one end than the other.

Look – here is an egg rather thin at one end. I'll set it on the table-top, and give it a push. It doesn't roll off. It simply rolls round and round.'

'What use is that?' asked Tony.

'Well, suppose you were a bird like the guillemot,' said Uncle Jack, 'a bird that lays its eggs on the bare cliff-ledge, with the sea crashing far below. No nest for it – no protec-

A guillemot's egg. Its shape makes it roll round and round so that it is safe on the rocky ledge

tion – and the wind howling around. A round egg would at once roll off – but an egg this shape, narrower at one end than the other, simply rolls round and round on the little ledge, quite safely.'

'Very clever,' said Tony. 'And I suppose there's a reason for the colouring on eggs, Uncle Jack – the queer lines and dots and speckles?'

'Of course,' said his uncle. 'Speckled or blotched eggs lying in a nest are not nearly so easily seen as plain white eggs would be. The different markings on birds' eggs are are a kind of "camouflage", to hide them. You know how soldiers camouflage buildings and guns in a war, by planting all sorts of queer markings over them – well, the bird does the same for its eggs! They are laid marked with spots, speckles, and lines, and are very difficult for an enemy to see.'

The lapwing and its eggs

'But there *are* white eggs,' said Mollie, at once. 'The owl lays white eggs, and so does the kingfisher, because I have seen them both.'

'Yes,' said Uncle Jack. 'But both those birds lay their eggs in dark places – the owl down in a tree-hole, and the kingfisher at the end of a tunnel in the river-bank. Enemies could not see them, so there is no need to camouflage them – but the birds themselves *do* need to see them in the darkness – so the eggs are laid white in colour and the birds see them easily when they go to their nests.'

'It seems as if there is some very clever reason for every little thing,' said Tony thoughtfully.

'There is,' said Uncle. 'But it's got to be thought of.'

'Well, who thought of all these clever ideas?' asked

Tony. 'The birds didn't. Who planned everything for them, Uncle? Who worked out the shape of their eggs, and the markings, and how to build nests?'

'Ah, who?' said Uncle Jack. 'I'll leave you to think that out for yourself!'

CHAPTER TWENTY-THREE

A Few More Visitors

Now that the children knew the common garden birds so well, they were always on the look-out for new visitors. And one morning they saw two big black birds walking solemnly over the lawn.

'Look! What are those birds?' asked Tony. 'They are not the same, because one is smaller than the other.'

'The big one is the rook,' said Uncle Jack. 'Do you see his long, strong bare beak? You may always tell the rook by his *bare* beak at the base, where it joins his head. A crow, who is very much like him, has a feathered base to his beak.'

'What is the smaller bird on the lawn?' asked Mollie.

'A jackdaw,' said her Uncle. 'Can't you hear him saying "chack, chack!" The rook says "caw, caw". Now look – the jackdaw has just turned away from us – do you see the grey patch at the back of his blue-black head? The rook has no grey at all, he is black all over.'

'Good,' said Tony. 'Now I shall always know a rook from a crow, and a jackdaw from a rook. Bare beak for a rook –

feathered beak for a crow – and grey patch at the back of his head for a jackdaw.'

'Who is smaller than the rook,' added Mollie. 'Aren't we getting good, Uncle?'

'I don't know,' said Uncle Jack, with a twinkle in his

The rook with his strong beak, and the smaller jackdaw

eye. 'I'll just see. Do you notice those two birds on the lawn, father away than the rook and jackdaw? What are they?'

'Well, one of them is easy,' said Mollie. 'It's just a blackbird. But I don't know the other – it's a very dark-brown – a bit like a thrush.'

'It's a blackbird too,' said her uncle. 'But a *hen* blackbird! Ah, you're not so good as you thought you were, Mollie. You didn't know an ordinary blackbird!'

Mollie went red. 'You caught me there, Uncle,' she said. 'I really hadn't noticed that the mother blackbird wasn't black, but dark-brown. No – I'm not so good as I thought I was.'

'But you're getting better every day,' said Uncle Jack. 'Now look up in the sky? What's that speck up there?'

The children saw a tiny black speck far up in the blue sky. Mollie laughed.

'Oh, Uncle! ! How can we possibly see a bird so far away?'

'Your *ears* can tell you, if your eyes can't,' said Uncle Jack. 'Listen!'

They all listened – and down to them fell a loud, sweet warbling song, that reminded Mollie of the singing of her canary at home.

'It's a sky-lark!' she cried. 'How silly of me! I know that a sky-lark flies right up into the sky to sing his lovely song.'

'Yes – and I'd like you to listen carefully to the song, please,' said Uncle. 'It has such a lot of "S's" in it – a *sibilant* song we call it, because it seems to have so many "S" sounds. Listen!'

They listened. They heard what their uncle meant at once. Tony began to try and whisper the song.

'Swee-o, sis-sis-sis-swee-o!' he said. 'Sis-swee-o, sis-swee-o! Swee-o, swee-o, sis-swee-o! Yes – there *are* a lot of "S's" in the lark's song, Uncle Jack. It's lovely and *sibilant*. What a nice new word. *Sibilant*. I like it. I shall make up a sibilant sentence. Listen. Snakes hiss softly. Snakes hiss softly. That is sibilant, isn't it, Uncle?'

'Very!' said Uncle Jack. 'Now see – the lark is swooping down in circles. He is coming to find his nest in the field.'

'I shall watch where he lands and then go and find it,' said Mollie.

'You won't be able to find it,' said her uncle. 'The lark lands a good way from his nest – and runs to it through the long grass, so that no one sees where it is.'

'Birds are too clever for me,' said Mollie. 'Oh, look –

The skylark

there's another bird we don't know Uncle – it's like a little brown mouse, running up that tree-trunk!'

'I was wondering when you or Tony would notice that bird,' said Uncle Jack, smiling. 'He has been in this garden every day for at least two months – and you haven't seen him!'

'Well, he isn't easy to see,' said Tony. 'What is his name?'

'His name tells you what he does,' said Uncle. 'He creeps up the tree – so he is called a tree-creeper! Easy isn't it? He creeps round and round tree-trunks and branches,

The tree-creeper hunts for small insects in the bark
of trees to feed his young

hunting for the little hidden insects that he loves to eat.'

They all watched the tree-creeper. He was a small bird,
brown above and silvery-white below. His beak was long
and curved, to help him to probe in the bark for his food.
He let the children come quite close to him, for he was not
a bit afraid. Round and round the trunk he went, in little
darts like a mouse. When he had finished hunting round
one tree he flew down to the foot of the next one, and
began to go up that in spirals, too.

'Well,' said Tony, when the tree-creeper flew to the next
garden. 'That's four more birds we've learnt today! Rook
– jackdaw – lark – and tree-creeper!'

'And *one* more,' said Uncle, smiling at Mollie. 'The *hen*
blackbird!'

CHAPTER TWENTY-FOUR

'Cuckoo!'

ONE fine warm morning, in the middle of April, Mollie came rushing indoors in excitement. 'Uncle! Aunt Jane! Listen, there's the cuckoo!'

They all listened. And, on the spring breeze, came the pretty double-call. 'Cuckoo! Cuckoo! Cuckoo!'

'Yes – the cuckoo's back again,' said Uncle Jack.

'I'm glad,' said Tony. 'I love his call. It sounds like summer.'

'It does,' said Aunt Jane. 'But I can't imagine why we give such a welcome to a bad bird like the cuckoo!'

'*Bad!*' said the children, in surprise. 'Why is he bad?'

'Well, the cuckoo is very lazy,' said Uncle Jack. 'He is the only bird who doesn't build a nest for his eggs.'

'Well, what does he do with them then?' asked Mollie, in surprise.

'I know!' said Tony. 'He puts them in some other bird's nest.'

'But doesn't the other bird turn out the cuckoo's egg?' asked Mollie.

'No,' said Uncle. 'The cuckoo is clever enough to remove one of the eggs from the nest, when its own egg is put there, and the bird doesn't seem to notice the stranger egg!'

'I wish I could see a cuckoo's egg in another bird's nest,' said Mollie.

'Well, you may perhaps be lucky enough to do so,' said Uncle Jack. 'I'll keep a watch and see if I think the cuckoo is laying near here.'

Uncle Jack did keep a watch. The cuckoos sometimes flew over the garden, and the children were surprised to see what big birds they were.

'They have dark bars across their chests,' said Tony. 'I think I should know a cuckoo now, if I met one.'

'Well, come and meet a cuckoo's egg,' said Uncle Jack. 'There is one down the garden.'

He took the children to a big bush, and parted the green twigs. In the middle was a hedge-sparrow's nest, with her pretty blue eggs.

'Another hedge-sparrow's nest,' said Uncle Jack. 'This, I think, is the second batch of eggs, or else a very late first sitting. Birds often raise two or three families, you know, in one summer.'

'Which is the cuckoo's egg?' asked Mollie. 'They are all small and blue. I expected an enormous egg, Uncle, because the cuckoo is such a big bird.'

'Yes, it is certainly a big bird,' said Uncle Jack, 'and yet it lays a small egg – and the egg matches the eggs of the nest in which the cuckoo lays its own egg. It is true that it doesn't always match them very well, but, as you see, it matches them well enough to make you wonder which it is!'

'I think I know which it is,' said Tony. 'It's that one in

the middle – the one that isn't quite so blue, and a tiny bit bigger than the others.'

'That's the one,' said Uncle Jack. 'Now we must come away or the hedge-sparrow will desert her nest. No – don't touch the egg, Mollie. Never handle eggs in a nest, for the

The newly hatched cuckoo throws out the egg of the hedge-sparrow

mother-bird will know they have been touched and may desert them at once.'

'Some children *take* the eggs from the nest,' said Tony. 'That must make the mother-bird very unhappy.'

'It does,' said his uncle. 'Even one egg should not be taken, because, you see, the bird will know that its nest has been touched, and may desert the rest of the eggs in fear. Come away, now – and we'll come back another day to see if the cuckoo has hatched.'

They all went back later on in the month – and they saw a curious thing!

'Good gracious!' said Mollie. 'There are no eggs – and only one baby-bird! What has happened to the others?'

'I'm afraid this little cuckoo has thrown them all out,' said Uncle Jack.

'Really! How horrid!' said Mollie, in surprise.

'You can't exactly blame *him*,' said Uncle Jack. 'He knows no better, and has to do what his nature tells him to. But you are right – it is not a pleasant thing to do – to turn out the rightful owners of the nest, and keep it for himself!'

'How did that ugly, little black bird do it?' asked Tony. 'Look at him, Uncle – quite bare and black, not a feather on him!'

'Do you see that hollow place between his little shoulders?' said Uncle Jack. 'Well, he uses that when he turns out baby-birds or eggs. He works himself about in the nest until he gets a bird or an egg into that hollow, then he climbs up the side of the nest, and tips out his load. Crash! It falls to the ground below. The baby cuckoo falls back into the nest tired out with his work.'

'Does he tip out *all* the eggs or birds?' asked Mollie.

'All of them,' said Uncle. 'He can't bear any egg or baby-bird with him. He is only happy when he is alone.'

'But what do the mother and father birds say when they come back to the nest and find their babies on the ground, or their eggs broken?' asked Tony.

'It's a strange thing – but the parent birds don't seem to notice either the broken eggs or the little lost birds,' said Uncle. 'They get prouder and prouder of the big baby cuckoo, who grows – and grows – and grows!'

'I'd like to see him grow,' said Mollie.

'Well, you will,' said Uncle Jack. 'We'll watch him.'

So they watched the little monster grow. He grew feathers. He grew very big indeed. He filled the nest. He cried loudly and piercingly for food all day long. The other birds could not bear to hear him calling so loudly, and they

The enormous baby cuckoo being fed by the hedge-sparrow

came to help the busy little hedge-sparrows to feed their enormous child. The robin came with worms. The chaffinch came with grubs. And even the song-thrush came, with an enormous woolly-bear caterpillar. The baby cuckoo loved that, and yelled for more. He was dreadfully noisy.

At last the nest was too small for him. He climbed out of it and sat on a branch. He tried his wings. They took him along clumsily.

'Look! The baby cuckoo is in the garden!' said Mollie.

'He's on that tree over there. What a noise he makes!'

He cried loudly. He grew every day. Soon he was far bigger than his foster-parents, the little hedge-sparrows. Then, so big was he, that the hedge-sparrows had to stand on his shoulder to feed him! The children thought that was a very peculiar sight.

Then at last he flew away, and they saw him no more.

'Well, really, I'm quite glad,' said Mollie. 'The poor little hedge-sparrows were wearing themselves out, feeding that great, greedy cuckoo! I know what Aunt Jane meant now, when she said that it was funny to give such a welcome to a bad bird like the cuckoo!'

'All the same, it *is* a lovely sound to hear in the spring-time,' said Tony. 'I shall always love the call of the cuckoo, even if I don't much like the bird himself!'

CHAPTER TWENTY-FIVE

Birds from Far Away

THE children had not only been watching the cuckoo that spring and summer – they had been watching many other new birds too!

With the warmer days a whole host of new birds had appeared, and were filling the garden with their pretty calls and songs. It was lovely to hear them.

'Where have they all suddenly come from?' asked Mollie. 'We didn't see them on our bird-table in the winter.'

'No, you couldn't,' said Uncle Jack. 'They were miles away then – some of them even down in South Africa!'

'Good gracious! Why did they come here then?' asked Mollie.

'It's a long story,' said Uncle, 'but I'll tell you very shortly. You see, a great many insect-eating birds, such as the swallow, could not possibly find enough food to eat here in the winter – and so they leave us, and go farther south to warmer countries, where there are plenty of insects to be found. They leave us in the autumn, with a cold northerly wind behind them – and they return again in our warm spring days with a warm southerly wind to help them.'

'How do they know the way?' asked Tony.

'Well, that magic thing, instinct, comes to their help again,' said Uncle Jack. 'Very often the young birds, only

The black swift, the steel-blue swallow, and the small house-martin with white patches above and below

born in the summer, will fly off in a flock together in the autumn, with no older birds to guide them – and will find their way over land and sea for the first time, down to the warm countries they seek.'

'It's marvellous,' said Mollie. 'But why do they come back in the spring, Uncle? Why don't they stay down in the warm countries always?'

'Because this is their home,' said Uncle Jack. 'They were

born here, and at the next nesting time in the following spring, all the birds who left us long to come back and build nests and lay eggs in the places they knew when they were tiny. They are homesick! So back they come in their thousands.'

'Such a lot of different kinds,' said Mollie. 'I shall never know all the new-comers.'

The spotted flycatcher

'Well, you can easily remember the little brown and white spotted-flycatcher,' said Uncle Jack, pointing to a tiny bird sitting on a post. 'See him, Mollie? Now watch – he will dart around the garden to catch a fly, and then go back to his watching-post.'

Sure enough, he did! He darted up in the air after a fly, caught it, circled round, and flew back to his post to watch again.

'A flycatcher,' said Mollie. 'Yes – that's easy. And the cuckoo I know, too.'

'We heard the chiffchaff shouting his name over and over again in the trees,' said Tony. ' "Chiff-chaff, chiff-chaff," he said. He is a slim, little greeny-yellow bird, isn't he Uncle?'

'Yes,' said Uncle Jack. 'And there are its cousins, the different warblers, most of them in green and yellow – so alike in the greening trees, that it is too difficult for you to see which is which, the first year.'

'What I really *would* like to know is – *how* do you know which are the swallows, and which are the martins and the swifts, Uncle, when they fly in the sky?' asked Mollie. 'You so often say, "Look at the swifts!" or "Listen to the swallows chattering!" and really, I can't tell which is which.'

'It's very easy, Mollie,' said Uncle Jack. 'Now look over there, where the swallows are sitting on that telegraph wire. Do you see their steel-blue backs and wings, their pale under-parts, and bright chestnut throat and forehead? See their long, forked tails too, and hear their pretty chatter – "Feeta-feetit, feeta-feetit," they keep saying, over and over again.'

'Yes,' said Tony. 'But the swift looks very much the same to me, Uncle.'

'Well, he's not really the same,' said his uncle. 'He doesn't even belong to the same family! It is only because he lives the same free life in the sky, that he is made the same way, with sickle-shaped wings and long tail. Look – there fly some swifts, quite low – do you see how sooty-black they are, not steel-blue like the swallow? And their under-parts are not pale. Their tails are not so forked, either – and just hear their screaming voices! They screech, they don't chatter like the swallows.'

'Yes – I can see the difference now,' said Tony, pleased. 'It's easy when you point it out, Uncle. But look – which are *those* birds, flying over there?'

'Those are the cousins of the swallow, the house-martins,' said Uncle Jack. 'There is one way in which you can always tell them from the swallows, Tony – they have a big white patch at the end of their backs, where their tails begin. The swallow hasn't got that white patch – only his under-parts are pale.'

'Good,' said Tony, 'I shall remember. The house-martin's tail is much shorter than the swallow's, too, isn't it, Uncle?'

'Yes,' said Uncle Jack. 'Now look – which is that, swift, swallow, or martin, Mollie?'

'Can't catch *me*!' said Mollie. 'It's a swift, Uncle, sooty-black all over. It looks like a little anchor flying in the sky!'

'Right,' said Uncle. 'And which bird is *that*?' He pointed to one that flew near them, and Mollie knew it at once.

'Swallow!' she said. 'Very long, forked tail and pale under-parts.'

'And there's a martin!' cried Tony. 'I saw the white patch on its back!'

'Good children,' said Uncle Jack. 'Now you will always know which bird you are looking at, when you gaze up into the summer sky, and see dozens of sickle-shaped wings and forked tails tearing through the air. Swift – swallow – or martin – you will know them all!'

CHAPTER TWENTY-SIX

Goodbye, Swallows! Goodbye, Children!

THE summer flew by swiftly. The children watched all kinds of birds splashing in the bird-bath they had placed on the lawn for the birds. They became very clever at hearing all sorts of bird-calls and songs, and they tamed the two robins that hopped about the garden.

'I suppose we don't know *all* the birds yet, do we, Uncle?' asked Mollie.

Uncle Jack laughed. 'Good gracious,' he said, 'even I don't know all of them! You have still to learn about the woodpecker, the hawks, the kestrel who hovers over our field so often, the jays and magpies of the wood, the pretty pigeons, the hooting owls . . .'

'Oh dear! We'll never learn them all!' said Mollie. 'We'll have to come and stay with you again, Uncle, and you must show us all the rest of the birds – and take us to the seaside, too, and tell us about the gulls there. They all look the same to Tony and me, but I expect you would say there were lots of different kinds!'

'I certainly should,' said Uncle Jack, with a laugh. 'Well,

be content with what you know already – but always keep your eyes open and see how much more you can learn as the years go by. Bird-life is marvellous – eggs, nests, songs, the birds themselves – no one can ever know everything about them, but it is lovely to find out all you can.'

Swallows migrating, like a large black cloud

'I'm going to,' said Tony. 'One day I'll know them all. I'll write books about them. I'll make everyone in the kingdom know and love their birds!'

'That will be fine,' said Uncle Jack, pleased. 'I should be proud of you. I have loved having you here for a whole year, telling you so many things you didn't know. It will be very lonely without you when you have gone.'

'We don't want to go a bit,' said Mollie, almost in tears. 'We'll love being with Mummy and Daddy again – but

London will be horrid after the country. I shall miss all the birds so much!'

'You don't need to miss them *all*!' said Uncle, smiling. 'You may take with you your peanut feeder, your seed-hopper, and your tit-bell. You will find that the tits, the sparrows, and the robins, to say nothing of starlings and pigeons, will come to you freely, even in London! And in the parks you will see nearly all the birds you have seen here, in the garden and fields.'

'That won't be so bad, then,' said Mollie, cheering up. 'Oh, look, Uncle – whatever are the swallows doing this evening?'

The three of them looked up at the swallows. Aunt Jane came out to see, too.

'They are gathering together on the telegraph wires by the hundred!' said Tony. 'There are house-martins with them – but no swifts.'

'No – the cuckoos and the swifts, and many others, are already gone,' said Uncle. 'The swallows often stay later, if the weather is mild. But now it is time for them to go. There is a cold northerly wind this evening. I think they will all fly tonight.'

Even as he spoke, a movement ran through the chattering birds on the wires – and then, as if at a signal, every swallow and every martin rose into the air. They circled round once or twice – and then streamed off towards the south, like a large black cloud of smoke!

'They've gone,' said Uncle. 'Their migration has begun. They will be in Africa, catching flies in the hot sun there, before two weeks have passed. Goodbye, swallows! Come again in the spring!'

'Goodbye!' said the children, half-sad to see their summer friends go. 'Goodbye!'

And, when the next week came, another goodbye was said, for it was time for the children to go, too.

'We are migrating to London,' said Mollie, hugging her aunt. 'But perhaps we shall come back in the spring, too, like the swallows!'

'I hope so,' said Aunt Jane. 'You have been very good birds all the year – I shall be pleased if you return in the spring, with your call of "Aunt Jane! Uncle Jack!" We'll listen for you, and look out for you, shall we?'

'Yes,' said Tony, laughing. 'Leave out some sheets and blankets for us to make a nice nest with, Aunt Jane. Goodbye, Uncle Jack, we've loved everything! Goodbye, Aunt Jane!'

And off they went, back to London. What a lot they knew! I do wonder if they remembered it all?

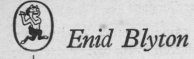

Enid Blyton

HELLO, MR TWIDDLE!　　　　20p

Meet Mr Twiddle, funny absent-minded
Twiddle – his memory is so bad he even loses
himself! You can't help but laugh at the scrapes
he gets into . . . (Illustrated)

WELL, REALLY, MR TWIDDLE!　　20p

What's to be done with Mr Twiddle? He is
so forgetful, he gets into some terrible
muddles . . . But you can't help liking him,
can you? (Illustrated)

True Animal Stories

These and other PICCOLO Books are obtainable from all booksellers and newsagents. If you have any difficulty please send purchase price plus 7p postage to PO Box 11, Falmouth, Cornwall.

While every effort is made to keep prices low it is sometimes necessary to increase prices at short notice. PAN Books reserve the right to show new retail prices on covers which may differ from those advertised in the text or elsewhere.